FROM

Darkness

TO

Dawn

MOSAICA PRESS

BRACHA PEARL TOPOROWITCH

FROM

Darkness

TO

Dawn

A STORY OF
struggle, perseverance,
and transformation

Mosaica Press, Inc.
© 2018 by Mosaica Press
Designed and typeset by Brocha Mirel Strizower

Published and distributed by:
Mosaica Press, Inc.
www.mosaicapress.com
info@mosaicapress.com

WITH LOVING GRATITUDE,
I DEDICATE THIS BOOK TO MY FATHER,

Yechiel Mechel ben Boruch Pinchus

(MECHELE RABINOWICZ) Z"L

WHO NEVER CUT CORNERS
AND DID WHAT HE FELT DUTY BOUND TO DO,
WHO NEVER SHIED AWAY FROM CHALLENGE
AND KNEW THAT HE WOULD OVERCOME,
WHO TAUGHT ME BY ALL THAT HE WAS ABOUT
STRUGGLE AND PERSEVERANCE.

AND TO MY MOTHER,

Feiga Malca bas Avigdor

(MALCA SCHOR RABINOWICZ) Z"L

WHO TAUGHT ME ABOUT DISCERNING AND ARTISTRY,
ABOUT HUMILITY AND GRATEFULNESS,
ABOUT CHESSED AND COMPASSION.
THANK YOU FOR GIVING ME WHAT YOU GAVE ME.

TABLE OF CONTENTS

ACKNOWLEDGMENTS

To You, *Ribono Shel Olam*, I send my overwhelming praise and thanks for blessing me with the talent needed for writing this book. My fervent wish is that it inspires others to connect more closely to You in their times of desperation and need, thereby enabling them to receive the resources necessary for overcoming their challenges.

To my husband and all the members of my precious family, who believed in me and encouraged me with my writing, my most loving thanks. Without your encouragement, I might have given up the project when the writing seemed endless.

To my daughters, Chana and Tehilla, my thanks from the depth of my being for reviewing the manuscript countless times, providing me with invaluable insights and corrections, making the story more believable and true to the time period it was written in.

To Shifrah Devorah Witt, my first writing coach and editor, multiple thanks for pushing me to get the work done and for all of your insightful feedback and improvements in so many obvious and subtle ways.

To the wonderful members of the Mosaica Press team who enabled this book to make it to the market, crafted professionally and esthetically, I sincerely thank you. I hope this will be the first of additional projects we will produce together.

To my editor at Mosaica Press, Rabbi Doron Kornbluth, your expertise and skill in refining, molding, and enhancing the work deserves more than a line of thanks in the acknowledgments. I offer you my profound thanks for working so closely and patiently with me in producing the book just to my liking.

To my numerous teachers and mentors in the field of hypnotherapy who guided me in becoming a skilled professional, I send my boundless thanks. Helping people in this amazing way is gratifying beyond words.

And lastly, to all my students and clients who taught me more than I ever taught them, thank you from the bottom of my heart for putting your trust in me. You gave me the material from which to construct the characters of this book, to understand suffering and comprehend how one becomes a survivor.

May the lessons culled from this story and integrated into any of my readers' lives generate merit that will hasten the coming of Mashiach and end all suffering forever more.

CHAPTER ONE

Living in Israel

B'nei Brak, Israel, 1972

THE CALL

The strident ringing of the telephone penetrated my sleeping mind with a seemingly relentless urgency. I groggily picked up the receiver while glancing at my watch. Who had the audacity to call at three p.m., the traditional *shluf shtunda* — siesta hour in Eretz Yisrael? My frustration at losing a well-deserved nap was evident as I spoke into the phone.

"Hello! Who is it?" I said sharply.

"Hello, it's Josh. I'm sorry to say this, Mrs. Perlman..." His voice shook as he continued, "Rabbi Perlman had an accident on the trip."

"What did you say? I don't understand!" Either my sleepiness or my subconscious prevented me from comprehending the words.

"Rabbi Perlman fell in the wadi."

"The what?"

"In the wadi, Wadi Kelt, on the trip! He's in the hospital."

Josh had to repeat his story several times before I finally understood.

"What happened to him?" I was almost screaming.

"He's in Hadassah Ein Kerem Hospital in Jerusalem," he answered, avoiding my question. "The doctors want to speak to you. They want you to come as soon as you can."

"Josh, tell me, what's wrong with him? How is he?"

"He's unconscious but in stable condition. He's in intensive care." His words tumbled out hurriedly, before his discomfort prevented him from telling me. "Bring Rabbi Perlman's tefillin and anything else you think might be necessary. The doctors need information about any medical condition or allergies that Rabbi Perlman might have. They need to speak to you as soon as possible."

I sucked in my breath and tried to stay focused. I couldn't lose it, I had to function.

"How do I find him?" I finally asked.

Josh gave me the details of the building and ward, needed to locate Chaim in the massive hospital complex. I scribbled down the information quickly on a scrap of paper.

"Mrs. Perlman, the boys are all saying *Tehillim* for a *refuah sheleimah*," Josh awkwardly tried to comfort me. "Don't worry! It'll be OK."

When I hung up the phone, I was in a daze. Was I dreaming or was this real? Not risking the consequences of going back to sleep, I groggily dragged myself out of bed. Despite the heaviness in my limbs, which felt like a load of bricks being pulled uphill, I dressed quickly and stood in front of the mirror with my *sheitel* in hand. I stared in shock at the face reflected there, unable to recognize myself. My normally high and smooth forehead was furrowed with deep creases. The dark hazel-green eyes, my best feature, were contorted by stress and fear, causing them to lose their delicate almond shape. And what had happened to my beautiful mouth? The full red lips that were almost always adorned with a gentle smile were now set in a hard, thin line. The only part of me that hadn't disappeared was the small, slightly upturned nose that had always made me look younger than my twenty-seven years. This new face that had abruptly replaced the old one looked a full ten years older. It spoke to me of the fear of the unknown, of helplessness and despair.

At least my hair hasn't turned white. I sighed as I arranged my shoulder-length auburn *sheitel* on my head. The soft waves surrounding my face reminded me of who I was.

I couldn't allow myself to break down. I had to get to Yerushalayim as fast as possible. The trip from B'nei Brak would take close to two hours.

My heart was racing and my brow was noticeably damp as I contemplated what had to be done before I left. I was confused about what to take with me, as I had no idea how long I would be at my husband's bedside. Would my stay last a day or a month or perhaps a year? Would our live-in mother's helper, Bassy, be able to manage the three children on her own?

Bassy had taken the children to her cousin's house to allow me to rest. Luckily, there was a phone there and I got through to her on my first try. I outlined the situation.

"Bassy, don't tell the children what happened to their father," I cautioned her. "Just say that I had to go somewhere and will come home as soon as I can."

"Sure, Sari! Don't worry. I know how to keep them busy and happy." She was doing a fair job of covering up the anxiety I could detect in her voice.

Bassy was a precious soul and I felt honored to be helping her move forward on her journey to full Torah observance. And as much as I was helping her, she was helping me negotiate life with three small children and one on the way. I loved living in Eretz Yisrael, but I still felt a stranger here despite the fact that we had made aliyah a year and a half earlier.

The thought of dealing with Israeli doctors in a hospital full of Israeli bureaucracy was overwhelming, almost more than I could handle. It was terrifying! Fear had always caused me to feel trapped, to become frozen, unable to function.

Suddenly, I was transported to Sea Gate in Brooklyn, in the summer of my ninth year of life. A scene flashed through my mind with lightning speed. I was hanging on to the outer side of the wooden beams of the boardwalk fence, staring at the white sand six feet below. If I wanted to go swimming, I had to jump — according to the weird command of our summer counselor. I knew I couldn't. The hot sun was burning my back. How long had I been standing there motionless, frozen in place, gripped by an irrational fear? My friends were flying off the boardwalk like birds released from a cage, whooping with joy as they hit the sand. I so desired to join them, but the fear was stronger. No amount of coaxing from my friends could break the shackles that bound me. I finally slunk home to our summer cottage, in shame and defeat.

I broke out of my reverie and shook my head quickly and determinedly from side to side. I then purposely turned my mind away from those suffocating thoughts and toward what needed to be taken care of at that moment. I gave Bassy some instructions in caring for the children and the house, and gave her my good friend Bina Reichman's number in case she needed help at home.

"Bassy," I tried to fake sounding strong and confident, while my stomach was tying itself in knots, "I have no idea how long I will be away; I'm not clear about Chaim's condition. Just as soon as I can, I'll get you help with the children. And you know that Hashem is always there, looking out for your welfare and sending you *malachim* to help you."

"I know, Sari, I know!" Her voice cracked for a moment. "Just take care of yourself and Chaim. We'll daven for you both!"

I wiped away the single tear that somehow found its way down my cheek. "Thank you, my dear Bassy! Every *tefillah* is totally appreciated and needed. I'll call when I know what's happening. Give yourself and the children a hug and a kiss from me. I thank Hashem from the bottom of my heart that you are with us and helping us in millions of ways. You're amazing!"

"*Refuah sheleimah. Refuah sheleimah!* Have a safe and quick trip!"

I hung up and moved into action mode. I packed the tefillin, some personal items of Chaim's, some food, and as much money as I could find at home. I decided I would take a taxi straight to the hospital, as public transport took forever, and emotionally I had no patience for buses.

THE DIAGNOSIS

When I got to the ward where Chaim was hospitalized, Dr. Daniel Tannenbaum,[1] an American physician and a trauma care specialist and neurologist, came immediately to the nurses' station upon being paged. He was tall and ramrod straight, exuding self-confidence. He was about sixty years of age. I was happy to see that he wore a yarmulke on his silver hair. He took me into his office.

"Please have a seat, Mrs. Perlman. I'd like to explain the situation before you go in to see Chaim."

His voice was kind and his manner considerate. His presence gave me a sense of security. I was especially lucky that this doctor could explain the situation to me in English so I could understand every detail.

"Chaim fell on the trail and rolled down a steep incline," he continued. "He is unconscious at the moment and has suffered a concussion. A scan of the brain shows that he has some minor internal bleeding. He also broke a few bones in his ankles and ribs. The fractures and the ugly facial abrasions are of no great concern. But a buildup of blood could put pressure on the brain and interfere with its oxygen supply. This could possibly cause brain and nerve damage very quickly. The next twenty-four hours are critical. It would be a very good sign of healing if Chaim regains consciousness during this time. If not, surgery will most likely be necessary. At this moment, it's too early to say how we'll proceed with treatment. We're waiting to see how things develop."

He paused to let his words sink in. I prepared myself. I could tell there was more to come.

"Most people completely recover from their concussions, but it might take months for the symptoms to disappear. In rare instances, one might experience permanent physical, emotional, neurological, or intellectual changes."

He looked at me kindly and I tried not to shudder visibly.

"Do you have any questions?"

"No, at least not yet." My voice was barely above a whisper. I could not bring myself to ask what "symptoms" he was talking about. I needed time to allow myself to discover what that meant.

The doctor proceeded to ask me questions about Chaim's physical condition, allergies, and the like. I found it hard to concentrate on the conversation, as all I could think about was my being taken to the Intensive Care Unit to see Chaim for myself. Finally, I was given a sterile white gown and was accompanied into the small room where Chaim lay.

Josh, the student who had called me, was sitting on a chair near the bed. When I entered, he averted his gaze but mumbled some words of encouragement. He then rose to join the other boys who were sitting outside and saying *Tehillim.*

"Mrs. Perlman, this is my pager number, don't hesitate to call me if you need anything," Dr. Tannenbaum said with a pained smile. He assured me that Chaim was being given the best care possible. Then he too left. I spent a few minutes discussing the situation with the nurse before she departed to attend to her other duties.

Finally, I turned my attention to the figure lying deathly still in the bed. I approached him slowly, barely breathing, for a better look. He was connected to an intravenous drip and various tubes and monitors. His face was bandaged in several places and I was unable to see the extent of the injuries. It was hard to recognize him. I was too shocked to cry. I needed some privacy and some time to digest what had happened before I was able to release the buildup of emotions inside.

I pulled a chair over to the bed and sat down. I focused on the unbandaged parts, the nose and cheekbones, and slowly reconstructed a vision of his face in my mind. Yes, this was my Chaim, the one who had chosen me, Sarah Greenwald, to be his wife six years earlier. I remembered the amazing *hashgachah pratis* that had brought us together.

The principal of the school I taught in, Rebbetzin Pesha Twersky, was a relative of my mother's. She had been asked to act as a *shadchan* between a young man visiting the USA from Israel and a distant relative of ours, also bearing the family name of Greenwald. When Rebbetzin Twersky spoke to the girl's father, he informed her that, unfortunately, his daughter was no longer *frum*.

Disappointed that she was unable to help the young man, a stranger in the USA, the Rebbetzin wished she could find someone else for him. Suddenly, she thought of me, and it seemed to her, knowing what she did about both of us, that there was a good chance we would make a fitting match. Rather than saying that the original suggestion was not suitable, she would substitute me, Ms. Greenwald, for the other Ms. Greenwald and perhaps a match would evolve.

Excited about her brainstorm, Rebbetzin Twersky immediately approached my parents with the idea. His father was a rabbi in a small town in Northern Israel and the young man himself had impressive credentials from his mentors and friends. He sounded like someone with initiative and a joy of living. The stories we heard about him highlighted his kind nature, his willingness to help others and to earn money in interesting ways so as to help needy people. My parents, after making the appropriate inquiries, agreed to our meeting. Although he spoke no English, we managed to communicate in my limited Hebrew and his limited Yiddish.

He was different from the typical yeshiva boy. He had his own independent way of thinking. He wanted to continue learning after marriage but also felt a great responsibility toward his fellow Jews and wanted to invest some of his energy into bringing nonreligious Jews closer to Judaism. I was intrigued.

Chaim Simcha Perlman was tall, quite thin, and very health conscious. Besides all that, he was strikingly intelligent as well as lively, charismatic, and funny. His jokes made me roll with laughter, even though I tried to suppress it. *After all,* I chided myself, *one should be serious when dating with the goal of marriage in mind.* But as serious as we were most of the time, we still shared a few good laughs together.

Despite the seeming language barrier, we became engaged. I was nearly twenty years old and Chaim was twenty-five. Rebbetzin Twersky was pleased with her matchmaking success, although sorry that I would be leaving my teaching job in her school. After the wedding, we planned to live in Lakewood, New Jersey, where the famous yeshiva founded by Rav Aharon Kotler was located.

Our life was almost idyllic. After a few years living there, we decided that moving to Eretz Yisrael would make our lives even better. So we did. Chaim was even happier back in the place he called home, and I was thrilled to be living in the Holy Land. Everything seemed so perfect, until...today, this tragic, catastrophic day.

Suddenly, the frightening sounds and sights of the ICU penetrated my consciousness, and I was once again sitting on a hard chair next to Chaim's bed.

Since I was now alone with Chaim, together with the noisy monitors, I decided to speak to him. I knew he would prefer hearing my voice instead of being subjected to the relentless beeping of the machinery.

"Chaim...Chaim, it's Sari. I came as fast as I could...Don't be afraid, Chaim. Dr. Tannenbaum is a great doctor and he assured me that you are being given the best care possible."

No response, not even the twitch of an eyelid!

I carried on bravely. Perhaps he would respond to the name his parents called him as a child. "Chaim'ke, Chaim'ke, before you know it there will be dozens...hundreds of people saying *Tehillim* for you.

Im yirtzeh Hashem, you'll have a *refuah sheleimah*…I know you will. Hashem can do anything!"

The words were choking me but I forced myself to carry on. Looking at him lying there, my resolve started to weaken. "You must wake up! Dr. Tannenbaum said it's critical…to wake up in the first twenty-four hours….Chaim, Chaim'ke, do you hear me? Wake up!!" My fists were clenched and I was biting my lips. I waited. No response.

I sat there quietly, davening for his healing for a long while. I couldn't bear to leave him, but there were so many things I had to take care of. Reluctantly, I made the decision to go.

"Chaim, I'm sorry, but I have to go now! I have to make phone calls to the *rav*, and Abba and Ima. I want them to say *Tehillim* for you…I'll be back soon, just as soon as I can. One of the boys will stay with you until I return."

I had no way of knowing if Chaim heard me or not. I knew that the sense of hearing is very acute and is the last sense to leave an injured person. I'd heard stories of people who had come out of their comas and repeated things that were said to them while unconscious. I hoped that my words had given Chaim the impetus to wake up, and perhaps a measure of comfort and hope. If not, at least I felt better doing what I could to help him break out of the coma.

I left the room and saw Chaim's students seated together in a huddle, all fervently saying *Tehillim*, some of them crying silently. I was deeply touched by the sight. I called to them and they quickly swarmed around me.

"Boys, thank you for staying here all these long hours and davening for Rabbi Perlman. I can't tell you how much I appreciate it!"

"It's nothing, Mrs. Perlman." "It's the least we could do." "We'll do anything to help!" Numerous similar sentences reverberated through the air, expressed by the group of young men.

"Boys, what happened? How did he fall?"

Chaim had taken his teenage yeshiva students on a day trip. He was not required to do so, as he was off duty during summer intersession, but wanted to give the boys a good time — he felt they really deserved it. Their destination was Wadi Kelt in the Judean Desert. This was known as one of the most popular hiking sites in Eretz Yisrael, with about sixty thousand visitors a year. They were going to take a five-hour hike through a deep gorge with a swimming hole in it. The high canyon walls and water made this a pleasant refuge even in the heat of the summer. The plan was that after a day of hiking, climbing canyon walls, and swimming and picnicking, they would travel to Yerushalayim for *Minchah* and *Maariv* at the Kosel before heading home.

They all tried to tell me at the same time what had transpired, and it took some doing to finally piece the story together. It seemed that while on the path leading down to the wadi, one of the boys had become dizzy and faint from exertion. Chaim ran over to him to support him, but in doing so lost his footing and fell. He rolled down the rocky trail until a boulder arrested his descent. When the boys got to him they found him unconscious and bleeding. There was no way they could carry him out of the wadi on the narrow and difficult path, and he had to be airlifted by helicopter to the hospital.

I realized that Chaim had escaped death by the compassion of the Almighty. He could easily have rolled off the edge and into the abyss below. I whispered my words of gratitude and heartfelt thanks to He Who controls all of life's happenings.

I was shaken by what I had just heard and kept my voice steady by sheer willpower. "Boys, I have to make some important phone calls. Will one of you please stay with Rabbi Perlman while I'm gone? I feel better knowing that someone is watching the numbers on the monitor screens."

"Sure, Mrs. Perlman. We'll take turns," one of the boys said.

"Please wait for me until I return. I want to set up a rotation system for staying at my husband's bedside around the clock. It might take some time until our relatives get here to take over for you."

They assured me that they would stay as long as I needed them. I breathed a sigh of relief since I had no idea how long it would be before Chaim's family would be able to get to the hospital from Afula in the north.

I was afraid to break the bitter news to my in-laws but knew I had no choice. Chaim was a very beloved son, and his father and mother would be devastated when I told them what had happened. I didn't want to hurt them but they needed to know. I also needed them at my side since none of my family lived in Eretz Yisrael. Their love and support would help me survive this ordeal.

When I found the public phone booth after a lengthy walk through the notoriously long hospital corridors, I was dismayed to find a line of people waiting their turn to call.

I couldn't cope with the situation and actually felt faint. I was nearly six months pregnant, I hadn't eaten for many hours, and suddenly an extreme weakness flooded my body. I really did not know how I would last the next few hours.

I dragged myself back to the nurses' station to put a call through to Dr. Tannenbaum. He had impressed me as an extremely considerate person and I felt sure he would respond to my dire predicament.

He called back after a few minutes. I felt like Hashem was taking care of me.

"Oh, thank you so much, Dr. Tannenbaum, for calling back right away!" I was quick to express my gratitude.

"How can I help you, Mrs. Perlman?"

"Look, I'm at the end of my strength. I have to call Chaim's parents and our rabbi and I have to arrange so many things." The words were coming fast, like flash floods in the Negev after a storm.

"It's next to impossible to use the public phone. Could you please give me access to a private phone where I could make my calls? Otherwise I just won't manage!" I hoped that I didn't sound like I was crying because that was exactly what I felt like doing.

I will never forget his answer to me.

"Mrs. Perlman, I am so glad you gave me this simple way of lightening your burden."

My words of thanks sounded terribly inadequate in the face of his unbelievable sensitivity. If only all doctors behaved in a manner that so beautifully expressed their humanity!

He then asked to speak to the nurse at the desk. After a moment, she led me into a private office with a phone.

"You can make calls anywhere in the country but not overseas," she stated simply.

"Oh, thank you so much!" The tears that appeared suddenly in my eyes expressed more than my feeble words could. She left and closed the door after her.

Was this the same Sari Perlman, née Greenwald, who in the past had been frozen into inactivity by her own exaggerated fears?! Who could never express what she needed and wanted? Who could never speak up in her own defense? Where had I found the audacity to ask for a private telephone in a public institution? It was unreal!

And then I realized something that shook me to the core. Hashem's ways are wondrous! Only He could send us those specific challenges that have the potential to bring out the best in us, to form us into who we are meant to be.

ARRANGEMENTS

My hand shook as I dialed the number. My mother-in-law picked up after three rings. I had practiced what to say to her in Hebrew, but in the stress of the moment the words disappeared like footprints washed away at the edge of the seashore.

I davened, "*Hashem sefasai tiftach* — open my lips (in just the right way)."[2] I forced my mouth open, because it was clenching in opposition to what I had to do next.

"Ima, it's Sari. How are you?"

"Sari! How wonderful to hear from you!"

"Ima, I'm sorry to have to tell you this." It seemed that Josh had said those very same words to me, ages ago. "Chaim was on a trip with his students. He…he fell and got hurt!"

"What! Are you serious? What happened?"

"I'm in Hadassah Ein Kerem Hospital with Chaim. He broke a few bones when he fell and rolled down the trail." I could hear her gasp. "Ima, I want you and Abba to come so we can take turns staying with Chaim."

"Of course, *metukah,* we'll come! But how does he feel? Is he in a lot of pain?"

"No, Ima, he's not in pain. The doctors are taking very good care of him."

"Oh, *baruch Hashem, baruch Hashem*! Chaim could never handle pain very well!"

I scolded myself silently, *Sari, you have to tell her! You can't let her think he's in the hospital because of some broken bones and then she finds out he had a concussion and is in a coma and might need brain surgery. You have to tell her now!*

But how could I? It had always been so hard for me to speak up, to say what had to be said. Always so shy and insecure, afraid of saying the wrong thing; in times of stress the words inevitably got stuck in my throat. And even though I desperately wanted to get them out, I would remain silent.

Silence was my friend; speech was my enemy. I could hide in the silence, never having to prove myself in any way. It was safe. I could not understand the source of my exaggerated shyness in early childhood. Neither of my parents or my three siblings suffered from it, but for me, it was as real and stubborn as if I was born with a lock on my lips. Probably my dyslexia, which had caused me to read very slowly and always fail my spelling tests, was a contributing factor. But when I was in school no one knew much about dyslexia, and so I suffered with my disability for years without being understood or given help to overcome it.

As clear as day, I envisioned the forlorn first grader that I once was. It was recess time and we were playing games with our teacher outside. As I crossed the yard, I noticed something dark on the ground. I bent to pick it up, unnoticed by the others. It was a black cloth wallet with some money inside. I realized that it had probably fallen from the pocket of one of the girls. I put the wallet in my pocket and planned to give it to the teacher. But my shyness was stronger than my will, and I found myself unable to approach her and tell her what I had found.

A short while later, Matty Schwartz discovered her loss and ran to the teacher to tell her about it. Morah Leah called the girls together and asked if anyone had found Matty's wallet. I desperately wanted to give it to her, but again, my shyness, like a heavy chain keeping me rooted in place, prevented me from coming forward. I now had the added shame of not having given the wallet to my teacher as soon as I'd found it. The more the teacher asked us for the return of the wallet, the more my guilty feelings ballooned and the more impossible it became to break open the seal on my lips. I imagined everyone's eyes staring at me knowingly, and I felt the wallet burning a hole in my pocket. Yet I was completely helpless to change the situation. I hid that horrid wallet in my drawer at home, never telling a soul about it. One day I finally had the courage to throw the despicable thing away, an object of my shame and lowliness.

The vision faded but I knew that I was no longer a six-year-old child unable to deal with her character flaws. Hashem had very graphically shown me what I needed to do.

"*Three deep breaths, Sari, and you'll do fine!*" my inner guide instructed me.

"Sari, are you there?" My mother-in-law sounded concerned.

"Yes, of course, Ima. I'm here. I was just reviewing what the doctor told me about Chaim's condition. You see…"

"Yes, Sari?" The tension in her voice was palpable.

"Unfortunately, Chaim hit his head."

"No!" The single word burst forth like a pebble from a slingshot. "What happened?"

"He's unconscious, but he'll probably wake up any time now."

I tried to sound convincing but I don't think I did a very good job. I could hear her sobbing quietly.

I wanted to comfort her, but frankly felt I couldn't. I felt the pressure of the myriad things I had to do. My words tumbled out quickly.

"Ima, I have a lot of calls to make. I haven't even called Rav Scheinerman yet to arrange for people to say *Tehillim* for Chaim. And Abba can tell the people in his shul to say *Tehillim* too.

"Yes, of course!"

"I wish I could continue talking to you, but when you come we'll talk. Please bring me some of your delicious home-cooked food and a change of clothes. I don't think I'll be going home anytime soon and I didn't bring much with me."

I gave my mother-in-law the phone number of the nurses' station in case she wanted to call me and instructions for finding our ward, and I hung up. The call had been emotional and very draining. But I was pleased that I'd been able to do it.

I made my other calls as quickly as possible, including a call to Bina Reichman. I wanted to hear the comforting voice of my dear friend. I also needed to inform her husband, the principal of the yeshiva where Chaim was employed, about the accident. It didn't seem likely that Chaim would be returning for the next semester.

Bina calmed me as best as she could. She let me know that she planned to come to spend time with me at the hospital and to alternate with me so that I could get some rest. Most importantly, she said she'd arrange a place for me to sleep that night. True to her word, she called back within a few minutes.

"Sari," she said, "my cousin Tova Weiss lives close to the hospital. She said you could use her guest room for as long as necessary. Here's her address and phone number."

"You're a lifesaver, Bina! What would I do without you?" I exclaimed as I wrote the numbers down.

"That's the least I could do. Is there anything else I can help you with?"

"Bina, maybe you can call Bassy and see if she needs help with the children. I left before they got home from their outing."

"No problem, Sari. I'll send my Shifra to sleep over. I'm sure Bassy will feel better with someone there with her."

"Bina, how can I thank you? You're a real angel!" The tears popped into my eyes unbidden. I felt grateful, helpless, and uplifted all at the same time.

I then called our very special and holy *rav*. I was lucky to get through to Rav Scheinerman and tell him all that had transpired.

"*Hisyatzvu ure'u yeshu'as Hashem* — stand erect in your faith and you will see the salvation of Hashem before your very eyes."[3]

He immediately gave me a surge of strength by quoting Moshe Rabbeinu's words to the desperate Jews standing at the edge of the Yam Suf. He reiterated for emphasis, "Keep your faith in the Almighty strong and you will see miracles happening, just as B'nei Yisrael experienced them throughout their history.

"Chaim will get well in due time," his deep voice intoned slowly. "I will daven and instruct my congregants to say *Tehillim* for a *refuah sheleimah*."

Hope flooded me. Like bolts of energy, hearing the words coming from the holy mouth of the *tzaddik* invigorated me and dispelled the dark cloud that had engulfed me.

"In case there are any medical decisions to be made," he added, "such as performing surgery or implanting a shunt for drainage of fluids, please call me immediately. And do inform me of any changes in your husband's condition. Write down my private number."

I wrote the precious number down on the back of my checkbook and then he hung up.

In addition to his spiritual status, Rav Shaul Scheinerman had a great deal of medical knowledge and was very often consulted over medical issues. I felt much more confident and at peace knowing that I was not alone, that I had the support and backing of a great person.

After thanking the nurse once again for use of the office, I bought a cup of coffee to drink with the cookies I had brought along. My small repast was not the quality of food that I was used to eating, but I had to make do. It was time to return to Chaim and let the boys go home.

Back at the ICU, things were stable and there were no apparent changes in Chaim's condition.

I turned to the sober group of Chaim's students. They had risen at dawn in anticipation of an exhilarating day and must now be exhausted beyond description.

"Boys! You've done more than enough. You can go home now. Someone from the family will soon be here to relieve me."

"No, Mrs. Perlman," one of the older boys said. "We'll wait here until someone comes. You shouldn't be here alone." The rest of them nodded in agreement.

I knew that one of them was probably feeling guilty for his part in the accident and I had no idea who he was. But as a group they all felt responsible to some degree for what had happened, and wanted to share the burden with me.

"That's really kind of you all!" I said with emotion. "Well, if you are staying, maybe someone can go to the grocery and get some food for us."

"Sure," Benny said quickly, happy to be helpful in some way. "What should I buy?"

I wrote out a list and gave him some money. I didn't want to have to live on coffee and cookies until my mother-in-law brought me some decent food. And I knew that growing boys were always hungry.

After Benny left, we all continued saying Tehillim. That was the best we could do at the moment.

At about eight p.m., my in-laws arrived with two of Chaim's brothers.

"Ima!" "Sari!" we exclaimed simultaneously as we caught sight of each other. I fell into my mother-in-law's arms and we both burst into tears. It was the first time in all those hours that I had expressed my distress. It was good to release my emotions and to have someone to cry with and to empathize with me.

I was truly lucky that my mother-in-law was so warm and understanding. She had eased my transition from the close-knit community of Lakewood to Eretz Yisrael, simply by accepting her American daughter-in-law just as she was. I wasn't able to get to know her or my father-in-law well during their short visit to the States for the wedding. But as soon as we met again in Lod Airport (later renamed Ben Gurion Airport), after a four-and-a-half-year separation, I felt I had found a friend and ally in this new phase in my life.

I remembered so clearly awakening that first morning after the flight. We were in the Perlmans' home in Afula and it was late morning before I awoke. I got out of bed, not quite remembering where I was. Looking out the window, I was stunned by the beauty of the scene. The citrus trees were a creation of visual pleasure, with their dark green leaves, their fragrant white flowers, and luscious yellow and orange fruits. Tropical-looking plants spread their foliage throughout the grounds, and the winter flowers splashed their colors about freely. There were brown and speckled hens roaming about a small enclosure, clucking contentedly. The hills in the distance were a rusty-gray color, and the sky was an azure blue. Fluffy white clouds drifted slowly past without the slightest hint of rain. A splendid sun shone brightly and warmed the window pane upon which I leaned. Several different bird sounds floated in the air and blended together into a melodious symphony. The scene was like a picture, a pretty postcard, too beautiful to believe. It held a promise of wonderful things to come and invited me to discover what they were.

Rabbi and Mrs. Perlman had been living in Afula for over thirty years and most of their eight children had been born there. Chaim's father, Eliezer Boruch, came to Palestine from Lithuania together with a group of Novardok Yeshiva students in the early 1930s. After marriage, he moved to Afula with his new wife, became the rabbi of a small shul, and founded a *yeshiva gedolah*.

Mrs. Perlman, Recha Bruckstein from Poland, came to Palestine in the 1920s, a fiery idealist ready to make the desert blossom.

After marrying, she settled into the traditional wife-mother role, and helped her husband with the shul business and fund-raising for the yeshiva.

We'd spent about a month in the Perlmans' home before moving to B'nei Brak, where we'd chosen to live. I saw my in-laws quite infrequently after that but we managed to keep up a close relationship. And now "Ima" was here doing her best to take care of me.

She had brought a delicious cooked meal for me and the boys. I was ravenous, as were the boys, but I was careful to speak to her as I ate. Thoughtful lady that she was, she had also sent one of her girls to be with Bassy and the children. It was such a relief to have someone helping me take care of things.

The boys left soon after, but declared that they were ready to take turns at their *rebbe's* bedside whenever we needed them. I jotted down some of their phone numbers, just in case, and blessed them with a safe journey home.

By now, I was literally drooping. My mother-in-law could see how exhausted I was.

"Sari, you look completely drained! It's time for you to go to sleep in that room your friend arranged for you. I prefer to spend the night in the hospital. I'll alternate with the boys, and when I become too tired I'll find an empty bed to lie down in. Abba plans to sleep at Uncle Meyer's house and relieve everyone first thing in the morning."

"Thank you, Ima. As soon as I speak with a doctor or nurse, I'll go."

After hearing that there was no change in Chaim's condition, I decided that getting some sleep would be the best thing I could do. I didn't want to collapse and, G-d forbid, become the next patient in the Perlman family.

Once again, I entered the room where Chaim lay. I could see no change in his facial expression or on the numbers on the screens.

"Chaim, I spoke to Rav Scheinerman," I whispered to him. "He said he'll daven for you and he'll tell all his hundreds of followers to daven...And he said that you will get well, Chaim! You will get well!"

I waited a full minute. Not the slightest glimmer of a response. Finally, I said, "Chaim, I'm going to get some sleep now. Ima and the boys are staying with you...I'll be back in the morning...*Refuah sheleimah b'meheirah!* Good night."

Finally, at ten p.m. I took a taxi to Tova Weiss's home. I decided to call my parents, as I could not do so from the hospital. Tova helped me put through a collect call, and I tearfully told my mother what had happened. She assured me that she would come to Israel as soon as she could arrange the trip. I was terribly grateful. I needed a mother's support and unconditional love.

I now understood what it meant to be bone-tired. I had never felt this tired in my life. I hoped my emotions wouldn't prevent me from sleeping. I didn't have to fear that, however, as sleep overtook me the moment my head hit the pillow. I was still in too much of a state of shock and confusion to recognize the danger Chaim was in and the extent of the upheaval his accident would create in our lives. I totally believed that the *Tehillim* so many people were saying for his recovery would bring about a positive outcome. I fell asleep without fear, albeit feeling deeply worried for Chaim's welfare.

I woke up suddenly in the depth of night in a severe state of panic. I remembered the doctor's ominous words that the first twenty-four hours after Chaim's injury and ensuing concussion were critical. It would be a sign of healing if he were to awaken within that time. And if not...I dared not think what the medical outcome might be.

I began trembling and chastised myself for sleeping when every moment of time was of essence. I jumped out of bed and washed *negel vasser*. I then took my pocket *Tehillim* out of my bag and determined to recite the entire *Tehillim* with deep concentration before going back to the hospital. I would find time to sleep later on.

As I recited the potent words of *Tehillim*, composed by our great king and teacher, Dovid Hamelech, I felt they were a salve applied to my wounded heart, and for all peoples' distress and despair in every generation till the end of time. How fortunate to have this support in our moments of need, like a floating plank to grab onto in a stormy sea! Just holding the small volume in my hands with its precious contents was comforting. Enunciating the words with all of their hidden meanings was food for my soul. I felt calmed from my previous feelings of panic. I knew we were in Hashem's hands and He would bring about the outcome that was best for us all.

But then I suddenly remembered something that I had learned once in relation to *kriyas Yam Suf* — the splitting of the Red Sea. When the Jews were standing and crying in front of the sea in trepidation of their imminent fate, Moshe Rabbeinu davened to Hashem to save them. Hashem responded to Moshe with, *"Mah titzak eilai....V'yisa'u* — Why are you crying out (praying) to Me? Tell B'nei Yisrael to travel, to walk into the sea!"[4]

What message was Hashem giving us by telling Moshe to stop praying? Isn't that what Jews do in their time of need — cry out to Hashem? Isn't that what Hashem wants of us?

The amazing explanation that I had learned was that sometimes praying alone is not enough. Sometimes the *middas hadin*, the attribute of justice, is so great that a lot more than praying is needed in order to overcome it. Before He would split the sea for them, Hashem wanted a display of their readiness to act with complete *mesiras nefesh*, putting their lives in danger in order to prove their trust in Him. Hashem wanted them to walk into the sea before it split, thereby demonstrating their unshakable belief that He could do anything and would save them.

Maybe I too had to demonstrate a total belief in Hashem by doing some act solely for Him, for His *nachas ruach*, His pleasure. I needed to do something that went against my nature in order to show that I was completely subjected to His will and, thereby, I had the right to ask Him to go against the laws of nature and save my husband.

I pondered this thought and wondered what I could take upon myself that would accomplish this goal. I knew that before the day was out I would make a decision to do something that expressed my complete, loving dedication and submission to the Almighty G-d. I felt in the deep recesses of my heart that it should be in the area of *tzniyus*, modesty in dress and refinement in various aspects of life. I felt somewhat lacking in that area. On the spur of the moment, I determined to wear longer skirts, thicker stockings, and cover my *sheitel* with a hat or scarf. I had no idea if this was something Hashem wanted of me, but some inner voice compelled me to make this decision.

I continued my recitation of *Tehillim* and managed to complete it all. I felt greatly at peace, imbued with the knowledge of Hashem's loving-kindness in every situation of life. I then quickly dressed and davened *Shacharis,* took something to eat from my kind hosts, and returned to the hospital. I was not prepared for what met me there.

SURGERY

When I had left the night before, Chaim's situation had been serious but stable. His vital signs had been normal and the prospects of his coming out of the coma shortly were good. When I walked into his ward in the ICU, I found all the family there, standing outside his room. My mother-in-law was crying and my father-in-law was engrossed in deep, meditative *tefillah*. I was greatly alarmed and my heart began beating unnaturally. I felt woozy.

I hurried over to find out what had happened. I found myself standing next to Chaim's brother Shmuel

"Shmuel, what's going on?"

Despite being only seventeen, he gave me a clear and accurate answer.

"The doctors suspect the onset of a brain hemorrhage and are in the process of assessing the damage," was his frightening reply.

Suddenly, there was a flurry of activity with doctors coming and going. A doctor scanned the group, spotted me, and came over. He put a clipboard in my hands and extended a pen toward me.

Pointing to a line on some form that stared at me, he said, "Mrs. Perlman, sign here. We need your consent to perform emergency surgery."

"What?!" I nearly shouted. "I have to call my rabbi first before I can consent."

The doctor looked me straight in the eye and said coldly, "Any delay could endanger your husband's life. You have to decide now, or take the risk of irreversible damage to Chaim's brain and life."

I could feel the blood draining from my face and imagined my complexion turning deathly pale. I was never able to make decisions easily and certainly not ones of such magnitude. And now I was being asked to make a life-and-death decision. I felt incapable of facing the situation and began shaking with fright.

I was thrust back in time, and felt myself shaking with fright from that night when I was eighteen years old. As one of the nine editors of our high school graduating-class yearbook, we had to choose compositions and art work from the students for inclusion in our magnum opus. Several teachers supervised us, one being Rabbi Levinson.

The editors wished to include a touching short story of an orphan and his stray dog, but Rabbi Levinson did not approve of it, claiming that a dog was a nonkosher animal and should not be the companion of a Jewish child. This was a cause of great chagrin and heated debate among the girls, but the story had been censored and the person in authority was not about to change his mind. The editors had to grin and bear it. Or so I thought.

The yearbook was finally printed and ready for distribution. Graduation was a few nights off. It was just past ten p.m. when my friend Breindy called.

"Do you know what's going on with the yearbook?" she asked.

"What do you mean?"

"You know how angry the girls are with Rabbi Levinson?"

"Sure I know. So what?" Breindy could tell that I had no clue of what was going on.

"Listen, I have to tell you something. I don't think you're going to like this."

"What are you talking about?" I was getting nervous.

"Sari, didn't you hear the editors talking about getting even with him? Didn't you see them plotting something?"

"No! I have no idea what you're talking about!" I screamed in frustration.

She then told me that one of the girls had written a beautiful poem and had cleverly embedded within it some unbelievably derogatory words, via a code system, deriding our esteemed rabbi. This creative work had been approved for inclusion in our yearbook. It seems that the editors, excluding me, knew of this revengeful scheme and now they and some of our classmates were having a good laugh over it.

I felt faint. How could this be? How could a few disgruntled girls incite all the others to agree to something as lowly as this? Why was I, one of the editors, not included in the plot? Obviously, they knew that I would never agree, and so they kept it a secret from me. I couldn't even fathom that it was really true.

"Breindy, are you sure? I can't believe it!"

"Sari, don't you have a copy of the yearbook at home?"

"Yes, I do."

"I'm coming over and I'll show you."

Breindy was at my house within ten minutes and she pointed out the poisonous message very cleverly revealed by taking the first letter of every sixth word of the poem. I was speechless.

"Breindy, what should I do?" Unable to think clearly, I turned to my friend for help.

"You have to tell Rabbi Nullman and let him decide what to do. I think that some of the yearbooks were already distributed today, but most of them are going to be given out in school tomorrow."

"I should tell Rabbi Nullman? I'm so ashamed that this happened! How could they have done it?! And how can I tell on the girls? What will happen to them?"

I was in a dilemma. If I tattled on my schoolmates, I would incur their unbridled wrath and they would probably never forgive me. To let the yearbook be distributed as it was, with its badge of shame on our class for all eternity, was an equally serious matter. As an editor of our yearbook, I had a responsibility to see that it was a work of impeccable Jewish standards. Would I be the one to take responsibility for the entire grade, nearly two hundred students, for what a few of them had done? Why, oh why, did Hashem give me this test?!

Breindy could practically hear the thoughts rolling about in my brain. Clearheaded as always, she spoke up firmly, "Yes, you have to tell Rabbi Nullman or have this on your conscience forever."

I couldn't wait for the next day to do something because it would be too late to stop the distribution of the yearbook, which had already started. I had to respond that night.

Yes, you have to tell Rabbi Nullman.... The words reverberated in my mind, over and over again. How could I possibly tell? How could I speak up?

Images from the past floated through my mind. I saw clearly the six-year-old, clutching a cloth wallet in her pocket, the speech frozen in her vocal chords. Then the ten-year-old floated by, facing someone who had played a bad joke on her, incapable of speaking up for herself. The eleven-year-old joined the group and stood out in stark relief, unable to break away from the stranglehold of her "best friend" who always took advantage of her. The twelve-year-old was equally vivid, running away from camp when she found it impossible to voice her pain after being forced into an unfair situation. Interspersed were the images of the girl playing the part of a horse in the camp play, happy at not having to speak any words, and another time playing the part of a boy who was unable to talk to humans, but could easily talk to animals. Many other images floated by, each concretizing the picture of someone who could not speak.

Isn't this who I am? I asked myself. *Someone who can't speak?* Reluctantly, I came to the realization, *No, I'm not that person anymore.* Just as with my dyslexia I had been able, with stubborn persistence, to rewire my brain, I knew I could also uproot this debilitating flaw. I knew I had to speak up and protest.

My parents weren't home to discuss things with. Seeing no option available, I thanked Breindy, sent her home, and, shaking with fright, called Rabbi Nullman, our administrative principal, and told him what happened.

I didn't sleep that entire night, knowing what I was to face the next day in school. After showing Rabbi Nullman the incriminating words, the yearbooks were collected and the sickening page cut out. I felt like a leper that no one wanted to get close to.

Over the years, I pondered whether I could have responded in a better way. I came to accept that as a teenager with limited resources, I had done the best I could with the tools I had. And so I forgave myself and hoped that all concerned had forgiven me too.

All this flashed before me. Could I take action now, as well? The clipboard, clutched tightly in my grip, was hurting my fingers, and the form I had been asked to sign floated before my eyes. I could not escape through reverie the decision begging my attention that very moment. I looked toward my father-in-law. He showed me no indication of what I was to do.

Do the best you can with the tools you have, I told myself. There was no one to guide me. It was up to me.

I took the doctor's pen and signed with a bleeding heart. I didn't even ask him to explain what the surgery entailed. I knew we were in Hashem's hands and He had provided us with top-notch physicians who would carry out His will.

Dr. Tannenbaum came over to me.

"Don't worry. Everything will be fine, *b'ezras Hashem.* I will be the primary surgeon, although there will be many others assisting me."

"May Hashem guide your hands for a successful outcome!"

It felt strange, my giving this experienced surgeon a blessing, but the words were uttered spontaneously, like droplets of soothing rain on a hot and torpid day. I felt as though I had aged considerably over the last few minutes.

"Amen!"

"How long will the surgery take?" I asked quickly as he was turning to leave.

"Anywhere from four to six hours, depending on what we find."

"Please send someone to me to explain what the operation is all about and to update us as it progresses. I really need to know!"

"Of course." He was gone in the blink of an eye. I didn't see him again for the next eight hours.

We ran after Chaim's bed as he was wheeled quickly toward the operating suite. I wanted to bless him before he disappeared behind the cold metal doors, but there was no time. All I could do was transmit my words of encouragement and faith mentally to my partner in life, and hope that his soul would be strengthened by them.

We were directed to the operating room waiting area. It was already full of family members of surgery patients sitting on the edges of their seats, waiting for news of their loved ones.

I found two chairs for my mother-in-law and myself. My father-in-law found one in a corner where he would not be distracted by the people milling around, and took out his pocket Gemara to learn. Chaim's two brothers had still not davened *Shacharis*, and they hurried off to the hospital shul.

My mother-in-law took out her *Tehillim* and I did the same. But I suddenly reminded myself that not long before I had finished saying all five books of Psalms and now I had a resolve to carry out. I wanted to implement my decision before the *yetzer hara* would persuade me that I could start tomorrow or next week, or the one after, and in that way prevent me from actually ever getting to it. That was "his" way of causing us to lose our resolve and neutralizing the lofty decisions we often make in life. So I knew I had to do something right now, and turn my decision into reality.

"Ima, I want to call Rav Scheinerman and let him know what's happening," I told her. "I also need to call Bassy and speak to the children."

I stood up and she nodded her understanding.

"Do you want me to call someone for you?" I asked.

"No, dear, I'll call after we hear how the surgery went."

I then went to the nurses' station, hoping to get access to the office I had used to make calls from.

CALLS

I was lucky to find the same nurse on duty as the day before, and once again she led me to the same private office. I took a few moments to plan my words before calling Rav Scheinerman. I used the private number he had given me. He answered the phone himself.

"Yes," he said simply, in his deep and melodious voice.

I steeled myself to speak clearly, without breaking down. "Shalom. This is Chaim Perlman's wife. I'd like to inform the *rav* of the new situation. Chaim was taken for emergency surgery a short while ago."

"Please give me all the details." I could easily detect the concern underlying his words.

"First, I want to apologize that I did not call the *rav* before giving my consent to the surgery. The doctor said that any delay might cause irreversible damage to Chaim."

"What was the reason for the surgery?"

"The doctors discovered a brain hemorrhage. There was no time to give any more details. Dr. Tannenbaum said the operation could take between four and six hours."

"You did the right thing by not wasting precious time." I let out a sigh of relief upon hearing his words. I had been afraid that he might chastise me for not consulting him first.

"Please inform me of the details of the surgery and its outcome as soon as you have any information. I would like to speak with Dr. Tannenbaum myself. Do you have his telephone numbers?"

I gave him the phone and pager numbers the doctor had given me.

"*B'siyata d'Shmaya,* you will yet have many long and happy years together with your husband." He hung up.

The *rav's* kind words triggered my emotions, and I wiped my tears as I dialed Bina's number. She was the one who could help me implement my resolve, as she was planning to come to be with me in the hospital.

I was happy she picked up the phone right away.

"Bina, good morning. It's Sari."

"Sari! How are you? What's happening?!"

I was touched by her concern. I quickly filled her in on the situation.

"Bina, I feel the need to take something upon myself, to make some positive changes, in addition to all the davening. So I'd like you to bring me some things when you come here."

"Sure, Sari, no problem! Just tell me what you want, and I'll be happy to bring them." How lucky I was to have a friend like Bina.

"Please buy me six pairs of 40-denier stockings, and buy a nice brown head scarf. Then get my brown outfit from my bedroom closet."

Happily, she asked no questions and made no comments on my requests. I then directed her in finding some other items in my home that I needed, such as my toothbrush, my alarm clock, and odds and ends.

"One other thing, Bina," I added as an afterthought, "I wonder if you could perhaps bring me some healthy food, like hummus and sautéed vegetables. I don't feel much like eating, but I have to for my 'baby.'"

"Of course, Sari! I'm only too happy to help you! I'll get to you as soon as I can."

"How are Bassy and the children doing?"

"They're really fine. The children miss you, but they're happy with all the attention from everyone taking care of them."

"I was afraid to call them. I couldn't bear it if they would start crying and want me to come home."

"Relax! They're in good hands, don't worry!" Bina assured me. I was looking forward to her coming, to having her solid shoulder to lean on.

I remembered the first time we met. We had recently moved to B'nei Brak from Afula. It was hard settling in to a new country, a new language, and getting along with people with a mentality quite different than the American one I had known all my life. I also wanted to find an English-speaking kindergarten for the two older girls. I had no idea of how to go about doing that.

One day, when I was out shopping, I had the two younger ones in my big American double stroller, exploring the different shops in the vicinity. I decided to make some purchases in a grocery store and left the stroller outside while taking the children in with me. When I finally dragged myself out, with the shopping bags and the children hanging on to my skirt, I found a woman waiting by my stroller. I approached the smiling lady.

"Hello!" she said.

"Hello," I replied.

"Are you the owner of this beautiful stroller?" she asked in English. "I couldn't help but admire it."

"Yes, I am. I brought it from home, but it's a little hard to maneuver in the crowded streets of B'nei Brak...."

"You must be new here," she noted. "As soon as I saw the stroller, I knew this must belong to a new American in town. So I waited for you to come out of the store."

"Wow, that's so nice of you! We came to Israel right after Chanukah. We moved to B'nei Brak not long ago."

"*B'ruchim ha-ba'im!* Welcome! My name is Bina Reichman. What's your name?"

"Sari Perlman. We live on Damesek Eliezer Street."

"Where are you from?"

"We're from Lakewood. How about you?" I asked her.

"I'm from Chicago. But we've been here for eight years. I'm really glad to meet you. I run an English-speakers group. We meet once a month for a *shiur* and fun activity and we always do something special before *yamim tovim*. I'd love to have you join our group."

"That sounds great!"

I was amazed at my good fortune at meeting this woman. "Maybe you can help me find a *gan* for my daughters with an English-speaking kindergarten teacher? They don't speak much Hebrew besides making *berachos* and a little davening. And I really want to get them into *gan* to start interacting with children."

"I'll walk you part of the way home and I'll fill you in on what's available."

Bina was a treasure house of information. She knew every Anglo in town and everything about everyone. I immediately felt a bond with her lovely personality. We made up to meet the following Sunday for a cup of coffee together.

I thanked Hashem from the bottom of my heart for sending this amazing woman into my life. Imagine waiting outside the store for "the new American in town" because she wanted to get to know me and help me settle in. What a *chessed!* And that's why she ran the English-speakers group — she knew that some of the women without family in Israel were having a hard time. And she wanted to have a way to help them. Unbelievable!

As a result of Bina's input, I soon had Shoshi and Miri enrolled in their respective kindergartens. It didn't take long before they both went happily each morning. I suddenly felt that life had become so much easier, more settled, and structured.

I was grateful to Hashem for easing the transition into my new home, so different in lifestyle from the one I knew. I had a feeling that Hashem had started showering His blessings on me after I made a decision to look at life with a positive slant rather than a negative one. Before we bought our own apartment on Damesek Eliezer Street, we were living in a rundown rented one, with creaky doors and lumpy mattresses. I was feeling low, especially when I woke up every morning with a backache. It didn't take me long to realize that when I was in a foul mood I tended to be short-tempered with the children and my day never seemed to go right.

I had so wanted to move to Eretz Yisrael and knew there must be a better way to adjust to my new life. I reminded myself of the power of positivity that I had learned in *hashkafah* classes in seminary from one of our inspiring teachers. I then made a conscious choice to see the cup half full rather than half empty and to work on feeling constant gratitude to Hashem. That's when things started turning around in my life. Who can estimate the power of positive thinking?

The vision faded. I stared at the stark white hospital walls and ended my conversation with Bina. It was time to call Bassy and tell her what was happening. And, of course, I would have to talk to the children. I still wasn't sure what to tell them....

Shoshi, my oldest daughter of five years, was a very bright child and would certainly be wondering why I'd disappeared. I worried that she might even be imagining the worst. So despite my fears, I dialed my home phone. Bassy picked up almost immediately.

"Hello, Bassy. It's Sari."

"Sari, Sari! How are you? How's Chaim?" She sounded apprehensive.

"Sorry I didn't call before, but it's hard to find an available phone here and I don't have a lot of free time."

"It's OK. But I'm so worried. Bina told us something and I told the children that their father had fallen down and needed to go to the hospital. I hope it was alright to say that."

"Sure, Bassy, just right. How did the children react?"

"They were scared at first and wanted to talk to you. I said you didn't have a phone but you would find a way to call them soon. So I'm sure they'll be thrilled to talk to you."

"I'm also anxious to talk to them. First, I want to tell you that Chaim was taken for emergency surgery a little while ago. I'm not sure exactly why. I only have a few minutes since I need to get back to the waiting room in case the doctor comes out of surgery to talk to us. I just wanted to check on the children to hear how they are. Please, will you and the others say *Tehillim* for Chaim Simcha ben Recha?"

I could hear Bassy suck in her breath as I spoke. Her voice shook as she said, "Of course we will. *B'ezras Hashem*, before you know it he'll have a *refuah sheleimah!*"

"Amen! Are the girls awake? Can I speak to Shoshi now?"

"Here she is, right next to me. Hashem should give you strength, Sari!"

Kindhearted girl that she was, I could feel that the news had hit her hard. Since I had no way of knowing when I would get home, I had to rely on her caring for the children as best as she could with my sister-in-law and Bina's daughter. I knew that the situation was in Hashem's hands and that I needn't worry too much.

"Mommy! Mommy!" The tears filled my eyes as I heard Shoshi's voice on the line. "Where are you? I want to come to you?"

"Hello, sweetie! How is my big girl? Are you helping Bassy take care of the children?"

"Mommy!" She wasn't being put off with my casual tone and choice of words. "Where are you?"

"Abba fell down and was taken to the hospital in Yerushalayim. He has some broken bones and got a bang on his head. The doctors are fixing him up now with a little operation and I have to be here until he gets better and can come home. Bassy, Dodah Chayale, and Shifi will take you to the park and make food for you and put you to sleep till I come home. So I need you to be my big girl and play nicely with the children. OK?"

"OK, Mommy. Can I come to see Abba in the hospital?"

"Soon, my love, but not now. As soon as Abba can have visitors I will call you to come. But now I want you to stay at home and help Bassy with Miri and Yochanan. I want you to say Tehillim that he should have a very fast *refuah sheleimah*. Bassy will say the words out loud for you and Miri to say after her. You will all have a very big mitzvah and help Abba get well!" Shoshi enjoyed being the "big" one and I hoped my idea would calm her down and make her cooperative.

My words had the desired effect and her tone of voice changed immediately. "Bassy told me that Mrs. Reichman is going to you today. We're gonna make *refuah sheleimah* cards to send with her. Can you hang them up in Abba's room?"

"Of course! That will make Abba so happy! Shoshi darling, I love you so much and wish I could keep on talking to you more and more. But I can't stay on the phone long. Let me speak to Miri before I go back to Abba. Is she there?"

"Mommy, I love you too! And Abba too! I'm sending you kisses!" Then I heard four-year-old Miri's high-pitched voice, "Mommeeeeee!"

I exchanged a few words with her and with two-year-old Yochanan. I then spoke to Bassy again, telling her where to find the things I wanted Bina to bring to me.

The calls were over and I felt as heavy as lead. It was time to get back to the stark reality of sitting in a waiting room, watching the clock, and waiting to hear about the fate of my husband. How blessed we were that we had the words of *Tehillim*, like steadfast friends, to accompany us in our vigil. We also had the additional merits of taking upon ourselves deeds, pleasing in the eyes of Hashem, like giving tzedakah and doing acts of *chessed*. As the holy words of the Mishnah state: "Rabbi Chananiyah ben Akashia says: 'The Holy One Blessed be He, wished to confer merit upon Israel; therefore, He gave them Torah and mitzvos in abundance...'"[5]

VISITORS

My back ached from sitting still for so many relentless hours. I needed to stretch, to move around, or just lie down and elevate my feet. But I couldn't leave the room. My eyes were alternately glued to the door the doctor would walk through or were focused on the words of my *Tehillim*. The back-and-forth movement of my eyes was the extent of my muscular workout, and my back was protesting. I was in a lot of physical as well as emotional pain.

And then I felt a presence standing in front of me. I looked up into the warm brown eyes of Bina Reichman. I stood up and we embraced. I was too exhausted to cry, so I just leaned on her solid presence.

We sat down in a corner of the room and talked quietly. Bina noticed how pale I looked and told me I must eat. In a moment, she had filled a disposable plate with her delicious, freshly prepared food. She placed it in my hands and waited to see me begin eating. She then brought another laden plate over to my mother-in-law, and offered some to my father-in-law and brothers-in-law.

Then I noticed that Rabbi Reichman was speaking to my father-in-law. I'd forgotten that he was Chaim's employer, friend, and mentor in many ways.

After making aliyah, we had lived off the sum of money received from the Jewish Agency given to *olim* to help them transition into their new home. In most cases, new immigrants were in desperate need of the money given to them before they found their own source of income. The amount we were given had dwindled quickly. Chaim needed to find a way to support his family.

Bina's husband had opened a yeshiva in B'nei Brak for Anglo-Saxon *ba'alei teshuvah* called Shaarei Orah — Gateways of Light. After Rabbi Reichman got to know Chaim, he offered him a teaching position with the second-year students, ranging in age from seventeen to eighteen years. The yeshiva also ran an evening outreach program in Tel Aviv. The job that was offered to Chaim also required that he spend at least two nights a week in the yeshiva's Tel Aviv night *kollel*, to be available to learn with study partners on any Judaism-related subject of their choice.

This aspect of the job was quite a bit more challenging than preparing a class for the young and willing students in B'nei Brak. The night students would be coming for any number of reasons. Some of them came out of sincere interest to learn Talmud or Jewish philosophy. Some came out of curiosity to see what learning Torah was all about. Others came to be argumentative, to point out how outmoded the Orthodox way of living was. And then there were those who came with no particular motive, perhaps ending up there because a friend had pulled them along.

The Torah scholars catering to this medley of visitors had to be willing and patient to deal with any manner of personality. They had to be there out of a sincere love of Judaism and with an idealism for passing their heritage on to others less spiritually fortunate than they. They had to really care for their fellow Jews. Rabbi Reichman saw Chaim as a suitable candidate for becoming a mentor.

Chaim hesitated in taking the yeshiva job. He didn't have experience in formal teaching and felt insecure in that role. He enjoyed having the freedom to do things in interesting and spontaneous ways, and being part of a structured classroom setting wasn't one of them. Still, the night *kollel* in Tel Aviv attracted him. He believed that one-on-one with a study partner he could move mountains; dealing with all sorts of people was a challenge he relished. His work in *kiruv* during the Lakewood years had truly honed him for this type of work. Rabbi Reichman explained that he could not afford to hire two individuals for both tasks and if Chaim wanted employment in the night *kollel*, he'd have to take the day job as well. We needed the income, so he agreed.

The rabbi had built up a close relationship with Chaim during his time in the yeshiva. The accident had occurred while Chaim had been on a trip with the Shaarei Orah boys, and naturally, Rabbi Reichman was concerned and felt the need to be involved. I could hear him telling my father-in-law that he would help in whatever way possible. These were no empty words. Every bit of *protekzia*, the Israeli word for obtaining privileged and special treatment, was eagerly sought after. Rabbi Reichman had personal connections to some doctors and hospital administrators, and this might prove very useful for us.

I finished eating and asked Bina if she had brought me the items I had requested. She placed a large package in my hands. It felt heavy, as heavy as the decision I had made. Even though it wouldn't be easy, I knew what I had to do.

I stood up with the package in my hands. "Bina, could you please come with me to the ladies' room?"

"Sure, Sari."

I approached my mother-in-law and said, "Ima, I'm going with Bina to the ladies' room. Please send someone to call us if the doctor comes out of surgery to speak to us."

I wanted to use this opportunity, walking together down the long hospital corridors, to explain my resolve to my friend.

"Bina, you must be wondering why I chose this particular *tikkun*, why I chose *tzniyus*." She nodded, agreeing with my assessment of her curiosity.

"You know, I was shy and always felt inferior when I was young. I think that's why it became very important for me to look good in the eyes of others. I became very clothes-conscious, always striving to keep up with the latest fashions. Of course, I was still careful to keep the *halachos*, but looking 'good' was still a big issue for me. With Chaim's accident, I've realized that now I want to 'look good' in the eyes of Hashem and not be so worried about how I appear in the eyes of others."

I didn't express all that was on my mind but I intensely hoped that I would be able to free myself of the need for approval of others and only strive for the approval of my Creator. I wanted to create change in myself, not only in the way I dressed but also in the things I said and did.

"What do you think, Bina? Does what I just said make sense?" Her input was important to me.

"Sari," Bina replied, "I can't think of anything more important for a woman to do than to improve in this area of her life. I think you are amazingly courageous to take this step and I believe it will be easier than you think. Hashem will help you! Not that there was anything wrong with how you dressed before, but this is very exemplary of you. I wish I could follow in your footsteps!"

Bina's words warmed my heart. I needed to know from someone wise that I hadn't chosen something of little significance to work on. If this was to be my gift to Hashem, I wanted it to be meaningful. Bina validated my choice in the most potent way possible. For her to say that she wished she could do the same as me was better than receiving a Nobel Peace Prize!

"Bina, wait for me till I change. I want you to be the first to see the new Sari!"

She sat down on a bench near the entrance to the washrooms.

I took the package into the cubicle with me. Among the clothing I found the children's *refuah sheleimah* cards and pushed them quickly into my handbag. I would look at them later when I had a moment of free time.

Within a few minutes I changed my clothes and looked at myself in the mirror. I saw a sweet-looking young lady staring at me, appearing a bit perplexed.

"Don't worry! Everything will turn out all right," I told my reflection. She gave me a hesitant smile in response and seemed a bit more at ease.

My heart fluttered with pride that I had actually taken the steps to make this change in my life. I was now bedecked in my brown outfit with the long skirt that I had always rolled up at the waist in order to get the "right" look. My *sheitel* was covered with a nice-looking brown scarf, and I was wearing thicker stockings. I had exchanged my fashionable shoes for orthopedic slippers that Bina brought from my home. I felt much more comfortable, yet thought I looked about twenty years older in my new getup. I quickly decided that rather than feeling "old," I would feel "wise," as the elderly usually are.

I presented myself to Bina. "What do you think? Will my mother-in-law recognize me?"

"You look beautiful, Sari, like a more mature, self-respecting Sarah Perlman. I would choose you as my daughter-in-law any day!"

"Thanks, Bina. I know you're trying to make me feel good, and I appreciate it! It's surprising to me, but I do feel at peace with my decision. I'm a little nervous, though, what I'll feel like when people ask me about my head covering."

"Don't worry about that now, Sari. You have more important things to think about. Just know that Hashem is very proud of you!"

"Yes, I know...We really do have to get back. Maybe there's some news of Chaim." I felt the tension setting in again.

It didn't take us long to return to the waiting room. I walked over to my mother-in-law and asked her if she'd heard anything.

Her eyes flickered for a moment as she looked at me. *Does she register the changes consciously?* I wondered. She didn't say a word about them, accepting me as I was, the way she always did. She let me know that no one had come to inform us of Chaim's condition.

"It's nearly six hours since Chaim went into surgery," I said. "I'll go crazy if we don't hear something soon!" I began shredding the tissue I was holding into tiny pieces.

"Maybe Rabbi Reichman can get some information out of someone," she replied. "Can you ask Bina to—"

She never finished her sentence, as a doctor we recognized walked over to us. He wanted to know if I was Chaim's wife. When I nodded yes, he asked me to come with him into a small office adjacent to the waiting room. The others followed us. He offered my mother-in-law and myself a seat and sat down as well. Deep exhaustion was etched all over his face.

He spoke to us in Hebrew and I tried my best to follow the gist of his words.

"We're sorry that we couldn't give you a report any sooner. The operation was much more complicated than we anticipated and we were all working under great pressure. Although we're still in the process of finishing up — it will take an hour or more to complete — Dr. Tannenbaum asked me to explain the situation to you and what we've done."

Thank You, Hashem that Chaim is still with us, I thought, as I steeled myself to hear the rest, which I knew would not be easy to digest. I focused my mind on the doctor and what he was saying.

"As a result of Chaim's fall and the blow to his head, he developed several bruises to the surface of the brain, called cortical contusions or hematomas. They can cause bleeding in the brain and an increase in the amount of fluid within the skull, causing brain swelling. This intracranial pressure, if not arrested, can cause severe damage and even death."

I was having a hard time following the doctor's technical explanation but grasped the severity of the situation. I tried not to feel, but just to listen in a robotic fashion.

"The first goal of the surgery was to stop the bleeding. We did this by repairing the damaged blood vessels.

"In order to do our work, we remove a small portion of the skull, called the bone flap. We actually leave the bone flap off for a substantial period of time in order to give the swelling some place to go and allow the brain to expand without compression. We don't take that much of the skull off, just enough to reduce the pressure. We've also put in a shunt to drain off the excess fluids. Now the excess fluid will drain off someplace else in the body where it will not cause damage as it would inside the brain."

The doctor paused and then asked if we had any questions.

"How long will you leave the bone flap off?" I asked.

"That all depends on how quickly the brain swelling is reduced. We can only decide how to proceed upon observation of the healing process."

Rabbi Reichman posed his question. "How do you classify Chaim's condition? Is he out of danger?"

"Rabbi," the doctor emphasized each word, "continue to pray. We cannot know for sure if we have stopped all of the bleeds. Anything can happen within the next day or two, from continued healing to continued brain damage, and even worse. We did our part, but now G-d has to do His."

We all looked at him in stunned silence. What more was there to ask or say? The doctor had summed it up perfectly: Continue to pray!

"I have to get back to surgery."

"Thank you for your time and consideration," I managed to say.

We followed him out of the office and returned to the waiting room. Like one person, we all took out our *sifrei Tehillim*.

The words on the page were out of focus and I could not read them. My mother-in-law was sobbing quietly but I was too numb to cry. My thoughts chased each other around in my head. *Why is this happening? What does Hashem want from us? Have I done enough? What else can I do? What will I tell the children?* And so endlessly, on and on.

I suddenly felt terribly weak. I had been up for many long hours, since my predawn recitation of *Tehillim*. I was afraid that if I didn't lie down I would fall down.

"Bina," I whispered to my friend sitting next to me, "I feel faint. I have to lie down somewhere."

She became alarmed at how pale I was. With her arm around my shoulders, we went together to find someone to help us. At the nurses' station, Bina explained the situation to the nurse on duty. She was young and very kind.

"Come, I have just the place for you," she said immediately.

She brought us over to an empty waiting room. A moment later, she brought me a pillow.

"This should make you more comfortable," she said.

"Thank you so much. This is perfect!"

As soon as I lay down I felt a great relief. I positioned my head to relax the tension in my neck caused by looking down into my *Tehillim* for such a long stretch of time.

"Bina," I said, "I'm feeling much better. Go back to the others and tell them where I can be found if there's any news."

"I think I should stay with you, Sari."

"I'm really feeling better. It's OK, you can go."

"If you're sure you feel all right, I'll go quickly to tell them and come back with something for you to eat."

"Great! See you soon." I started saying the *Rambam*'s Thirteen Principles of Faith by heart. I had memorized them when I was in physical therapy years earlier for a slipped disc. For a period of half a year I went three times weekly for therapy and resented spending so much time taking care of my physical body. I decided to learn something meaningful by heart that I could recite during my time spent at the back clinic, and I had chosen the Thirteen Principles of Faith. Now I would bolster my *emunah* by saying them with deep concentration. Repeating the words over and over again calmed me down like a medicinal tonic. By the time Bina got back, I felt much improved.

Adhering to the halachic requirements, she had double-wrapped the food and put it in the nonkosher microwave oven to warm up. It took her some time to return.

"Sorry it took me so long, but I had to wait my turn to use the microwave." She began dishing out a plate for me.

"Bina, I'm really not hungry. I don't feel like eating now."

"Sari, you have to! I understand that you're probably not hungry with all that's going on, but you still have to feed your baby!"

"OK! OK, Bina, I'll eat, but only if you do too."

"Sure. I've been ignoring my hunger cues too!"

So together we ate and deeply thanked Hashem for our ability to eat. I was well aware that, *b'ezras Hashem*, when Chaim did regain consciousness, there could be areas of his brain affected by his injury and that some of his functions could be impaired. After all the *Tehillim* and Principles of Faith that I had repeated so many times, I had no doubts that he would regain consciousness. The question was when and in what state of health. In the meantime, I resolved to be very grateful to Hashem for all the bodily functions that most of us so casually take for granted.

"Bina, that was delicious! The food definitely did me a world of good. But I do think it's time we go back to the others."

We stood up together and I picked up the pillow to return it to the nurse. Then, on second thought, I replaced it, thinking that perhaps my mother-in-law could be persuaded to lie down.

I had purposely not looked at my watch for a very long time. I didn't want to be stressed by seeing how many hours had gone by since the beginning of surgery. But now, as we walked back to the waiting room, I could no longer restrain myself.

"Bina! It's already three-thirty in the afternoon. Chaim has been in surgery for seven and a half hours!"

"This was a complicated operation, taking a very long time to complete. You heard what the doctor said. Imagine repairing tiny damaged blood vessels!"

"But Dr. Tannenbaum said it would take up to six hours!" I retorted.

"Maybe he miscalculated. It happens all the time. He's probably finishing up now. Come on, courage, Sari!! You want to strengthen your mother-in-law. The calmer you look the more you will encourage her and the others."

"You expect me to be able to encourage the others?"

"I do," Bina answered very simply. "I know you have it in you to do that. I wouldn't say this to just anyone, but I'll say it to you. You can go in there and give your mother-in-law the support she needs. Just draw on your deep faith and your close relationship with Hakadosh Baruch Hu and you will become a pillar of strength. I can't explain how I know, but I know you can do it. It was something I picked up in you when I saw you dressed in the clothes I brought. You transformed."

I never expected to hear that and I was incredulous at her suggestion. Me, Sari Perlman, née Greenwald, a pillar of strength? I had always been the frightened one, incapable of action. I knew things had changed over the years, but not to that extent. There was no way that Bina's assessment of my current capabilities was correct.

But then I remembered myself back in Lakewood, with the group of women learning to be childbirth educators. I had already been preparing women for birth in the Lamaze method of natural childbirth for several years. I loved my newfound occupation and decided at some point to become professional, so I enrolled in a course for certification as a childbirth educator. Our instructor, Mary Walker, was a physical therapist from South Africa and we spent five days learning from her. For some reason, she really liked me and I quickly became the "teacher's pet." I couldn't imagine what she saw in me. But the fact was that she chose me as her partner when we broke up to work as couples, so apparently, she did think me special. She also encouraged me to stay in touch with her once the course was over, which I did for a while.

I had always thought this was just a random episode in my life of no real significance. But now I suddenly wondered if perhaps there was something, something about me, that made me stand out from the others.

I decided to pretend that Bina was right and try to live up to the role she had given me. A few deep breaths both invigorated me and calmed me down. I then walked into the waiting room and went over to my mother-in-law.

"Ima," I stroked her arm gently, "how are you feeling? Maybe you'd like to lie down for a bit, as I did. I feel so much better now."

"No, my dear, I can't leave. Maybe the doctor will come out and tell us something. How can I lie down now?"

"You know, Ima, I thought the same thing before. But then I almost fainted. We're going to be here for days, maybe weeks, and we'll need all the strength we can get. Even if you lie down for a few minutes it will make a big difference in the way you feel. And if someone comes out to talk to us, we'll send someone to get you right away. Come on, Ima, just for a few minutes." I helped her stand up and motioned for Shmuel to come over. Together, we walked with her to the room where I had lain down. The pillow was still there. She gratefully sank down onto the seat, lay her head on the pillow and fell into a deep trance. She nodded her head slightly when I asked if she was comfortable, but didn't move any other muscle.

I walked back with Shmuel and told him he should get his mother if there was any news.

A few minutes after we returned and I settled myself in my seat with my *Tehillim*, Dr. Tannenbaum walked in. I looked at my watch. It was exactly eight hours since he had left us that morning.

He looked tired but calm. I walked over to him. Bina was right behind me, and the others crowded around.

"I am happy to say that Chaim's vital signs are all in the normal range. His respiration is strong and the shunt is working well. We have done our utmost to repair the damage that was visible to us. Of course, he is in Hashem's hands and you will obviously continue to daven for him. But the physical signs are encouraging, and I have a feeling that he will make a good recovery. Within the next twenty-four hours we'll be able to tell which way his healing is going."

"Thank you for all you have done, doctor!" My words were uttered emotionally, and I truly believed he was a special *shaliach* from Hashem. "When can I see him?"

"Not for a while, I'm afraid. He will be closely monitored for several hours. If all his signs remain stable you will be called into the recovery room one at a time to see him. But I can't say when that will be just yet."

My father-in-law shook the doctor's hand, as did Rabbi Reichman, and they showered him with blessings. He then left us. Shmuel asked his father if he should wake his mother to tell her the news. Rabbi Perlman decided to tell her himself and walked out with Shmuel.

"Bina, I think that it's time for you to go home," I said to my dear friend. "You've done more than I ever expected."

"I'll go home after you have a good nap. I'll go with you to Tova's house and make some calls while you sleep. My husband intends to stay in the hospital and speak to some of the doctors and hospital administrators. He would also like to have a talk with Dr. Tannenbaum. He'll call us at Tova's house if there is any change in Chaim's condition and in case you can go into the recovery room to see him." Bina's advice made a lot of sense.

My father-in-law decided to go with his wife to his brother's home for a wash and a rest. They would then come back to the hospital before returning to Afula. Their two sons would stay in the hospital, taking turns at Chaim's bedside overnight. The following day, another son and son-in-law would come to relieve their brothers. My mother-in-law promised to send me cooked food with the boys. We hugged and kissed and parted ways for the time being.

Within a very short time, I was in Tova's house. I showered and fell into a cool, clean bed. I trusted Tova would wake me if needed and so I allowed myself to sleep.

CHAPTER TWO

Recovery

WAKING UP

Although I was exhausted, my sleep was fitful. Upon awakening, I did not feel refreshed. I craved the comfort of lying in bed, but knew I must return to the hospital. Who could know what awaited me there? On the one hand, I didn't want to find out; on the other hand, the need to know was pushing me out of bed.

I felt myself standing on the threshold of a new chapter of my life. *Where will it take me? How will my life and the children's lives be affected? How will I be able to give birth in the midst of this turmoil? How will I cope?*

I had to take life one step at a time, to focus on the moment and not on the unknowns of the future. I made a conscious decision to calm myself down.

There are too many questions without any answers, I told myself as I took slow, deep breaths. *Life will give me the answers in its own good time. I choose to stop thinking these unproductive thoughts and focus on positive ones instead.*

I suddenly realized how scared I was feeling. It was hard for me to formulate a clear and concise positive thought, a mantra that I could say repeatedly to calm myself down. I needed a role model.

One of my seminary teachers, Rebbetzin Meshulam, came to mind. She was the picture of deep *emunah* and calm in troubled times. I imagined myself being her, and in my mind heard what she would say in a situation like this. I was truly surprised that it only took a few seconds to transition into a calm state. The words flowed naturally and I said them out loud to give them more substance.

"I choose for my *emunah* affirmation: *'Kol mahn d'avid Rachmana l'tav avid* — all that the Merciful One does, He does for good.'[6] Everything in my life is sent to me by Hashem for my ultimate benefit. My *emunah* affirmation reminds me of this. This affirmation will become my constant companion and I will repeat it countless times throughout the day. In this way, I will remain calm and in control of my emotions. There is no challenge too difficult to surmount, and with Hashem at my side I will do so successfully. I will become a better person for it."

I certainly wasn't Rebbetzin Meshulam, but I could aspire to be. And so, even though my train of thought felt a bit artificial, a bit contrived, I knew these thoughts were true. If I could maintain focus on them, I knew I would actually become calm. And that is what I did.

As Bina and I returned to the hospital, my mother-in-law greeted us.

"Perfect timing!" she said. "We'll be able to enter the recovery room soon. The doctor said that Chaim's condition is the same, serious but stable. If it stays that way for the next hour they'll move him into the critical care ward."

My heart was beating fast as I walked in, the first of the group. I approached the silent, reclining figure in trepidation, afraid to look, yet intensely curious as to what I would find.

As I leaned over the bed to see him more clearly, my first reaction was, *Baruch Hashem, he looks calm. There is no sign of trauma or pain on his face. He actually seems to be enjoying a good sleep.*

His head was swathed in bandages and I was unable to see the size of the brain flap that had been removed. I knew that prior to surgery Chaim's head had been completely shaved but, to our good fortune, his beard was intact. I hadn't known there was the possibility of performing scalp surgery without the removal of all the facial hair. It seems Dr. Tannenbaum, a religious Jew, chose this option out of sensitivity to Chaim's needs and desires. So my husband looked more or less like the Chaim from before the accident, with the addition of a big white hat adorning his head, and several facial bandages. If one didn't know the details of his condition, it would be hard to fathom just how serious it was. It seemed that all that was needed was for him to wake up.

I pulled a chair over to the bed and sat down. I started speaking words of faith and encouragement. I believed that he could hear me and that my talking to him would help him come out of his coma. I knew that it was critical for him to wake up as soon as possible, and this would be a sign of healing.

"You know, Chaim," I said, "the children miss you so very much. They're wondering when their Abba will come home."

Suddenly, I remembered the cards they had made. I pulled them out of my bag and held them up in front of his face.

"See, they made you *refuah sheleimah* cards all by themselves. They're full of their love for you."

Can his neshamah see them through closed eyelids? I wondered. I wanted to create an emotional connection between him and this world, anything to draw him back to us. There was no flicker of his eyelids or movement in any part of his body other than the slow rise and fall of his chest. I resolved to repeat this and similar tactics for as long as it would take to rouse him.

My in-laws wanted to return to Afula, so I made my visit with Chaim short. I exited and they entered for a few minutes, speaking to him and blessing him. Then I walked them to the elevators and wished them a safe journey home.

Rabbi Reichman was inside the recovery room when I returned. It sounded to me that he was saying good-bye to Chaim for the time being, but promised to return within the next few days. I exchanged some words with Bina, thanking her from the bottom of my heart. Then they too left. I felt alone and vulnerable, as though the receding tide was leaving the seashore exposed and bare.

I turned to my two brothers-in-law, Shmuel and Yehoshua, and we devised a plan for the night. I would remain with Chaim for the next several hours until he was moved to the ward, while they went off somewhere to sleep. Then I would rouse them to remain with Chaim for the night while I went to Tova's house to sleep.

And so, the days carried on, with family members and close friends taking turns at Chaim's bedside, talking to him, davening, and learning Torah. Dr. Tannenbaum advised us to continue stimulating Chaim in whichever way possible, as this would encourage him to come back to us. I debated with myself about bringing Shoshi to talk to her father. I knew it would be a powerful stimulus for Chaim, but feared the effect upon her of seeing her father in a coma. I decided to wait a little longer.

One day, the third day after surgery, Rav Scheinerman appeared with some of his students. They learned for hours with their *sefarim*, in a circle around Chaim's bed. Chaim didn't respond in any way while they were there, but the next day he woke up.

THE EARLY PHASE

My sleep that night had been sweet, with the sounds of the learning at Chaim's bedside replaying in my mind. They had served as a gentle lullaby, rocking me to sleep. I slept well and rose early.

I had just returned to the hospital from Tova's house in the early morning hours to relieve my brothers-in-law. I walked into Chaim's room wearing my white sterile gown and cap and approached the bed.

"Good morning, Chaim," I said to him, as I'd said for the past five days. "How are you feeling this morning?"

Of course, I never expected an answer, but this was my way of treating Chaim's situation as a temporary interruption of his normal functions and feelings. I was completely shocked when he slowly opened his eyes, squinted from the light he hadn't seen for so long, and looked at me as if to answer.

He then opened his mouth and said in a very low voice, "Why are you dressed so funny, Sari?"

I nearly burst out laughing; that was the last thing I expected to hear. Then I realized that he had no idea of where he was or what had happened.

"Chaim! Chaim! You woke up!! Welcome back! *Baruch rofei cholim!*"[7] The words burst forth from my mouth. My brothers-in-law rushed back to the bed to see for themselves, with expressions of joy. I told them to get the doctor on duty.

By now I was crying from happiness and relief. Chaim looked perplexed upon seeing my tears. He needed an explanation and I had to give him one.

"Chaim, dear Chaim, do you remember taking the boys from yeshiva on a trip to Wadi Kelt?" I waited for some sign of remembrance, but there seemed to be none. I imagined that a certain amount of confusion or even amnesia would be normal. Yet he had recognized me and surely that was a positive sign of the state of his mind. So I continued explaining what had happened.

"You were on a hike with the boys and you fell and hurt your head. Now you're in the hospital recovering." I waited for a response, but there was none. "Are you in any pain?" I asked.

He seemed to be thinking about my last question. After a very long pause, he said, "No."

A doctor walked over to the bed with two aides and sent me out of the room. I hurried over to the nurses' station.

"Nurse! Nurse! Chaim woke up!" I burst out.

"That is absolutely wonderful news!" she responded.

"Can you please inform Dr. Tannenbaum?"

"He's in surgery right now, but I'll send him a message." She gave me an empathetic smile and turned to her messaging board.

"Thanks so much!"

I hurried off to the ladies' room. My emotions were in turmoil and my knees were shaking. One moment I was laughing and the next I was crying. Since I was alone in the restroom I allowed myself a good, loud cry. Within a few moments, I felt a great relief, after having released the built-up tension. I splashed cold water on my face and dried it carefully. I wanted to get back to Chaim's room and speak to the doctor who was examining him.

I hurried back to the room and wondered when my life would allow me to move through it slowly, without so much worry. All I seemed to have been doing lately was hurrying. I wondered if the stress I was experiencing and all the worry about Chaim would affect my unborn baby. I promised myself and "my baby" that at the first opportunity, I would take a nice, languid vacation, or at the least a calming stroll in the park. How I longed for that coveted moment!

I stood outside the door to Chaim's room and waited. Chaim's brothers stood nearby.

"Shmuel, Yehoshua, I want you to make some phone calls now to inform your parents, Rav Scheinerman, and Rabbi Reichman that Chaim regained consciousness," I instructed. "I'm waiting here to speak to the doctor when he finishes examining Chaim."

They ran off and I waited patiently while saying *Tehillim*. After about twenty minutes, the doctor exited. He led me to his consultation room.

"During this preliminary examination," he said, "your husband has been able to understand my questions and has even answered some of them clearly. He has amnesia at the moment, but that is expected. Hopefully his memory will return, but we cannot say how long that will take. There are other symptoms that he is suffering from. Dr.

Tannenbaum will give him a more comprehensive examination and then he'll explain to you in more detail what those symptoms are. He'll also design a rehabilitation program for your husband's healing. Additionally, he'll explain to you the long-term effects of the trauma to the brain and what you can expect in the future. There really isn't much more that I can add until the scans and other testing are done. But at least he woke up."

I sighed in relief. "Thank you, doctor. When will Dr. Tannenbaum be able to examine Chaim?"

"I don't know what his surgery schedule is this morning, but I'm sure that as soon as he's free he'll be here.

"In the meantime, you want to stimulate Chaim's memory by speaking of home, the children, and so on. Just be careful not to tire him out. His system still needs a lot of rest in order to recuperate. When you see him losing focus on what you are saying, encourage him to close his eyes and rest. Often, he'll fall asleep spontaneously and that's perfectly normal. Make sure that people speak quietly and don't make sudden noises. You want to gently encourage and never push too hard."

"Thank you so much, doctor. That makes sense."

The doctor left the room and I returned to Chaim's bedside. He was asleep. An expression of calm rested on his face. The nurse was checking his vital signs and then changed the IV bag. Chaim's nutrition was administered through IV and a gavage tube inserted in his nostril.

"Nurse, when will my husband be able to eat regularly?" I asked.

"I don't know! I just do what the doctor orders," she replied harshly.

Many of the hospital staff I had encountered were overworked and short-tempered. The nurse's words stung and I bit my lips in an effort to hold back the tears. I tried distracting my mind from her insensitivity by silently repeating my mantra. After a while, she left the room and I sat down next to Chaim. I wanted to make phone calls but could not risk missing Dr. Tannenbaum's visit. I searched my bag for pictures of the children to show Chaim when he woke. I was not one of those proud mothers who carried around an album of pictures of her offspring wherever she went. But luckily, I found a few crumpled ones of the children. Would Chaim recognize them, I wondered?

MEMORIES

I recalled reading somewhere that the most common form of amnesia after a brain injury affects the ability to form new memories, and does not affect the access of old ones. I suddenly remembered how my friend's grandmother couldn't recognize her young family members or remember what someone had told her a moment before — but spoke lucidly about her childhood memories. I decided that I would talk to Chaim about his childhood experiences and as he responded more and more, would slowly move forward in time, bringing to mind the more recent happenings in his life.

I hurried to the nurses' station to ask for paper as I determined to write down Chaim's most compelling childhood and teenage memories, stories I had heard him recounting many times over. In this way, others who were with Chaim when I was not there could read the stories to him and thereby jog his memory. I was sure my in-laws could add many more interesting tales to my account, ones I was unaware of. But for now, I'd start with what I knew.

Once I was again comfortably settled in my chair next to his bed, I began writing. I figured that if Chaim's mind was more in the past than in the present, perhaps he thought in simple language as well, and so I decided to write in language suitable for a child.

The stories of Chaim's childhood escapades always made us laugh. I managed to record a few before Dr. Tannenbaum appeared. I was so engrossed in writing that I didn't notice when he walked in. He caught me by surprise.

"What are you writing?" he asked.

"I'm recording some of Chaim's childhood memories for myself and others to read to him. I'm hoping they will stimulate his memory."

"Excellent," he said. "It's very helpful to bring up old memories in order to stimulate the brain after trauma."

His confirmation of the importance of what I was doing encouraged me, knowing that I wasn't wasting my time.

"Concussion commonly disrupts memories of the hours, days, or weeks before and after the injury," he said, "and most often will not affect the injured person's old memories, which are stored in a different part of the brain. Rest assured that amnesia from concussion or other mild head trauma usually resolves over time. However, the amnesia from severe head injury may not recede. We still need to discover the extent of any existing injury and which part of the brain might have been affected. This will decide our course of action in the healing protocol."

"How long does it take for the amnesia to disappear?" I asked him.

"Improvement is usually seen by six to nine months."

I gasped in shock. "What! It can take that long for him to get back to normal?"

"Mrs. Perlman," Dr. Tannenbaum looked at me with compassion, "pray to Hashem that he gets back to normal, no matter how long it takes. Brain swelling caused by brain bleeds is a serious medical condition. Unfortunately, in some cases the damage is permanent.

"Since he's sleeping, I can't conduct certain diagnostic tests. Instead, I'm taking him now for a computerized tomography scan that will give us a lot of vital information about the condition of his brain. We should be back in about an hour."

THE BRAIN SCAN

He paged someone and two aides appeared shortly afterward. They pushed Chaim's bed out of the room toward the elevators.

I decided not to accompany them as I wanted to speak to Rav Scheinerman and repeat the doctor's latest words to him. I also wished to ask him whether he thought it was a good idea for Shoshi to come and visit her father. I didn't only want the doctor's medical opinion, but wanted to hear what my *rav* had to say. I had to consider not only the positive effect of her visit on Chaim, but also if there would be a negative effect on Shoshi seeing her father in his present condition. Another consideration was that if Chaim did not recognize Shoshi, we'd all be devastated. Should we take that risk?

Once again, I made my way to the nurses' station. I didn't recognize the nurse on duty and her morose expression was rather intimidating.

Act as though you are making the most normal request in the world, I instructed myself determinedly, before fear could overtake me. *Don't get distracted by nasty people!*

I took a deep breath and said as pleasantly as I could, "Hello. Do you think I could use the phone from the private office that I used the other day? Dr. Tannenbaum has left instructions at the nurses' station about it."

"Yes, I'm aware of that instruction," she said acidly. "Come. But make it fast!"

She led me to the office and unlocked the door. I sighed in relief as she left the room. I sat down at the desk to write my list of whom to call and what to say to each one. I had no idea of where my brothers-in-law were and whom they had contacted. If they had gone to the public phone it was possible that they hadn't even gotten to the front of the line yet.

I kept the list short. My priority was to get through to Rav Scheinerman. I dialed his number with a shaky hand.

The number was busy. Unconsciously, I clenched my teeth and my shoulders went tight. I needed the *rav's* blessing, not only his words of advice and wisdom. I needed to be able to calm down.

I said *Tehillim* for five minutes and then dialed again. A wave of relief passed over me as I heard the ring of the phone at the other end. In a moment, I heard the deep voice of my *rav* answering.

"It's Chaim's wife from the hospital," I said in a trembling voice.

"Yes, yes. What is happening?" he asked.

"Chaim woke up this morning and spoke to me. He doesn't remember everything, but he understood what I was saying. The doctor took him for a brain scan now."

"*Baruch Hashem! Chasdei Hashem!* That is wonderful, wonderful news!" The *rav* sounded exuberant. "Did the doctor say anything to you about his condition?"

"Yes, he did." I had to choke back the tears. "He said that they still do not know the extent of the damage to the brain and it might take six to nine months for us to see improvement."

"I see. And anything else?" The *rav* knew that there was more just by hearing my voice.

"He said that in some cases of head injury there can be permanent damage. The scan will show him what part of the brain was affected and what type of damage there might be." I couldn't say anything else and waited for some words of hope and comfort.

"I see. So we'll continue to daven that Hashem send Chaim a speedy and complete recovery. There is nothing that He cannot do. Is that not true? We don't go by statistics. Hashem treats each individual in his own merit. Chaim has as much a chance of a complete recovery as another person has a chance for permanent damage. Is that not true?"

"Yes, of course," I had to admit. "It's just so scary to hear those words!"

"Hashem is simply testing your *emunah*. For Him, nothing is impossible. Repeat to yourself again and again, "*Hashem Hu haElokim, ein od milvado!*"[8] Chaim has so many of his own personal merits. Besides that, there are so many merits from all the *tefillos* that are being said and the tzedakah that is being given for his sake. You don't need to worry. Worry will not help you. But you must keep on davening with all your strength and believe that Hashem can make Chaim well, and do *maasei chessed* at every opportunity. And remember, in your case taking care of yourself is also considered an act of *chessed*, as you have a responsibility for another one as well."

"Thank you! Thank you for your words of encouragement." I felt much lighter, much more at peace. "I do have a question for the *rav*."

"Yes?"

"It is important to stimulate Chaim's memory. Does the *rav* think it would be a good idea to bring our oldest child Shoshi to see her father? It might help bring him back to the present."

"We need to first hear what the doctor says about Chaim's condition, and how much stimulation is good for him. It would also be better for Shoshi if her father recognizes her and can talk to her in a normal manner. First, show him pictures of the child to see how he reacts. Once he begins recognizing and remembering things and people, you can decide when to bring her to see her father."

"Thank you, that makes sense."

"Rest assured, *b'siyata d'Shmaya*, all will be well."

I wondered how the *rav* could be so sure. Not everyone emerged from their accidents intact. Perhaps he had some inside information that I was not privy to. On the other hand, "all will be well" could also mean that whatever happens in any given situation is the right thing for that person, and for him it is "well" — the way it is meant to be. Troubles and adversities are given to us by Hashem to build us, to develop us, and not to punish us. We don't always see it that way. If we did we would truly understand that "all is well" no matter what. Maybe that was what he meant. And wasn't that the true understanding of my mantra, "*Kol mahn d'avid Rachmana l'tav avid*"?

The *rav* continued speaking. "I will call Dr. Tannenbaum sometime this morning to hear from him directly what the tests show and how he intends to proceed. *B'ezras Hashem*, all will be well."

There was a soft click at the other end and our conversation was concluded. I felt much better, not so dependent on what the scans and tests showed. I would keep my mind focused, having a more positive outlook and greater faith in Hashem. Fear and worry certainly had no right to take up place in my mind.

I looked at my watch and decided to make fewer calls than I had planned on making. I had to hurry back. My calls were short and to the point.

My in-laws told me they would be coming to the hospital shortly and remain over Shabbos. I had forgotten that Shabbos would very soon be upon us. Where would I spend Shabbos? It made sense to wait to hear from Dr. Tannenbaum before making my Shabbos plans.

Bassy assured me that the children were doing fine, despite their asking for me.

I then called Tova, my very special hostess.

"Hello, Tova, it's Sari."

"Hi, Sari. What's happening?"

"Great news. Chaim woke up!!"

"Wow! That's amazing. I have some good news for you too."

"What?" I couldn't even remotely imagine what she had in mind.

"Your mother called to say that she'll be arriving Sunday evening."

"What? Thanks for the great news! I'm so excited!"

"Tell me, Tova," I continued, "is it possible for me to walk to the hospital on Shabbos from your place?"

"In your condition, Sari, I would say no. It's a very long walk."

"Then I'll have to sleep in the hospital. What do you suggest I do?"

"The local Bikur Cholim Society provides places to sleep in and around the hospital and prepares hot Shabbos meals at the hospital for those who need them. Just call the telephone number I'll give you to reserve a bed."

"Thanks so much, Tova. Thanks for all your help!"

She gave me the number. I then called the Bikur Cholim and arranged for a bed on the hospital grounds. They told me where I could get my *mehadrin* kosher meals. It would mean quite a bit of walking in the hospital, and dragging myself up and down the stairs, but thank G-d, a bed and food were available.

I returned to Chaim's room. Chaim's brothers hadn't managed to make any phone calls, as the phone was broken.

Before long, we saw Chaim's bed being rolled back toward the room. Dr. Tannenbaum was not with him. My stress levels jumped again; I had to speak to him! I needed to know what was happening with my husband.

Neither of the aides pushing the bed knew where Dr. Tannenbaum was. They maneuvered the bed into position, attached Chaim to the various monitors he had been disconnected from, and left.

"Welcome back, Chaim!" I said. "How was the scan?"

I waited for a response, but there was none.

"I'm sure we'll hear good news once your images are analyzed."

Chaim didn't move; he seemed to be asleep.

"Boys," I said, "please stay here while I try to find Dr. Tannenbaum."

I hurried (as always; hurrying because there was so much to take care of) to the nurses' station.

"Nurse, I absolutely have to speak to Dr. Tannenbaum before he leaves the hospital for the weekend. I think I'll go crazy if I don't hear what the brain scan showed."

She looked at me pityingly and said, "I'll do my best. If I get through to him, I'll call you to the nurses' station."

"Thanks so much!" I returned to Chaim's side.

The helplessness I felt caused me to feel anxious. I knew that I might be transferring my feelings to Chaim and certainly to my baby, which was not a good idea. As a childbirth educator, a big part of what I taught was how to relax.

I decided to guide myself into a state of relaxation. If the baby in the womb was calmed by the sound of the mother's heartbeat, maybe I could be calmed by the sound of Chaim's heart monitor?

I sent the boys off to the nurses' station to await their parents there and told them to let me know if Dr. Tannenbaum called in.

Now that I was alone in the room with Chaim, I made myself comfortable in the chair and began my meditation by slowing down my breath. I thought of all the encouraging words the *rav* had told me; I literally heard his voice in my mind. This gave me hope and a feeling of safety.

Then, as I continued my deep breathing, I created an image of a safe and beautiful place in my mind, which I explored, a place in which I allowed myself to experience total peace. I could feel the presence of Hashem with me there, taking care of me. The need to know what the brain scans showed vanished; they didn't matter at this moment. Hashem was doing whatever had to be done and my inner being knew that to be true.

My body was rejuvenating as though I was having a restorative sleep. I certainly was in no hurry to leave this pleasant and healing place. How long I was immersed in this altered state of mind, I couldn't tell; it seemed like five minutes.

I heard a voice calling, "Mrs. Perlman, Mrs. Perlman!" The nurse was shaking my shoulder to "awaken" me. I suddenly remembered where I was and looked at my watch. I was surprised to see that twenty-five minutes had passed since I had started my guided-imagery journey. I looked up into the nurse's inquisitive face.

"Dr. Tannenbaum wants to speak to you," she said. "He's on the line at the nurses' station. You didn't come when I paged you."

I followed her to the nurses' station and she handed the telephone receiver to me.

"Hello," I whispered.

"Hello, Mrs. Perlman. I'm sorry I had no time to speak to you face-to-face. There were too many things to finish up before leaving for Shabbat."

"I quite understand," I said.

"I don't really have much to tell you at the moment. The brain scans will have to be looked at carefully and analyzed by several specialists before we come to any conclusions. That was impossible to do today. Sunday we plan to have our meeting and make our decisions in terms of Chaim's healing protocol. What I can say, though, is that the swelling has gone down considerably over the past few days. That is a really good sign of healing. Just continue doing what you've been doing till now and we should see even more improvement. I wish you a wonderful Shabbat."

He sounded rushed so I held back from asking any questions. In all honesty, I did not feel as though I had any at the moment. I was still partially back in my safe and beautiful place, together with Hashem, in whose company I had no questions.

"Thank you, doctor. It was so nice of you to call me and give me this good news. I know we are in good hands." I wondered if he understood the double meaning of my words.

"You're welcome. Have a good Shabbat." He clicked off and I handed the receiver back to the nurse.

"Your in-laws have arrived," she said. "They've been here for about ten minutes."

I stood up and found them speaking to the boys. I nodded to my father-in-law and embraced my mother-in-law. She was shaking.

"What did the scan show?" she asked.

"I just finished speaking to the doctor and he was very pleased that the brain swelling has gone down considerably. On Sunday, a few specialists are having a meeting to analyze the scans and decide how to proceed. That's all he told me."

She let out a big sigh of relief, and I imagined a large stone rolling off her chest.

"*Baruch Hashem!* Come, let's sit down and figure out what we need to do before Shabbos."

"I'm going to learn at Chaim's bedside. It will be good for him to hear words of Torah again." My father-in-law pulled out a pocket Gemara from his jacket and walked off toward Chaim's room. Soon we could hear from the distance the sweet *niggun* men traditionally use when learning Gemara.

The boys had been told to stay in the hospital over Shabbos. They now went to their uncle's home to wash up and change their clothes. My in-laws had decided with the boys that they would alternate using the hospital beds they had reserved as they took turns staying with Chaim.

"Sari, you really could go home to be with the children for Shabbos if you'd like to. We have enough people staying over and it's more important that you are there."

It was tempting. I didn't know what to do. I discussed the various pros and cons of each option with my mother-in-law. We finally decided that I would remain in the hospital and the children would go to Chaim's married sister Bruriya for Shabbos. Going to Auntie Bruriya and Uncle Kalman was always a big treat for them. Hopefully that would make up for my absence.

Since Chaim was still sleeping and it was getting late, I decided to go to Tova's house to get ready for Shabbos. I also wanted to call my parents and give them the latest news, and wish the children good Shabbos. I packed up my things and left for Tova's house.

SHABBOS IN THE HOSPITAL

Surprisingly, Shabbos in the hospital was much better than I anticipated. I was able to sleep, the Bikur Cholim food wasn't bad, and, best of all, the men took turns singing *zemiros* next to Chaim's bed. Chaim woke up several times and smiled when he heard the singing. It seemed that he remembered what it meant. He even responded to some of our questions. We did a lot of talking to him; about Shabbos and the *parashas ha'shavua*, and he listened most of the time. I think we all felt a special holy atmosphere as we shared this Shabbos in a united effort to help Chaim. The one difficulty for me was going up and down many flights of stairs, which left me exhausted.

On *motzaei Shabbos* we had surprise visitors. Bina and Rabbi Reichman borrowed a car and drove out to see us. They slept over at Tova's house.

THE CHECK-UP

How I managed to get up in the morning I really don't know. Bina, unbeknown to me, had scheduled an important appointment in my name and she stayed overnight to be sure I showed up for it. The plaque on the wall read "DORA TURNER, MD, specializing in gynecology and obstetrics." After a lengthy wait, we were finally admitted into the doctor's office.

The examination was quite thorough. Afterward, sitting opposite the doctor, I was a little alarmed by her serious expression as she began speaking.

"I realize from speaking to Mrs. Reichman that you've been through a very stressful week, and this may or may not have affected your health. Your exam shows an elevation of your blood pressure, a fast pulse, and high sugar levels in your urine. The elevated pulse rate may be an indication of infection or the beginning of a virus. And probably, you haven't been eating or sleeping as you should during this time. You may be deficient in iron and other nutrients. I want you to do the following blood and urine tests and bring me the results tomorrow.

"Normally, I would tell a patient with these numbers to go on complete bed rest for a week or two, in addition to taking nutritional supplements and perhaps medications. But I'll wait to see all of your lab results before deciding on a course of treatment. In the meantime, you must make every effort to take care of yourself at this time, despite your need to do all you can for your husband. Remember, you have a responsibility for another life as well as your own."

I was shocked into silence. I suddenly realized that I actually felt very ill. Bina was discussing my case with the doctor and I decided that I would let her take the initiative in my care. I was just too tired to deal with it.

We left the doctor and went to the lab to do some of the tests. I would have to return the following morning after a twelve-hour fast to do the rest of them.

"Sari," Bina said, "the doctor did not think it would be advisable for you to come close to Chaim since you might be harboring infection. You could try talking to him from the doorway of the room. She suggested that you tell him that you have to go home for a few days to take care of the children."

Bina and I sat down with my mother-in-law and, after throwing various ideas back and forth, we came up with a plan. I would stay overnight at Tova's so that I could take the remaining blood tests the following morning and return to Dr. Turner with the results of the tests I had done on this day. Once all the results were in and the doctor began my treatment plan, we would decide if I should go home or not. But it was clear to all of us that I was not to enter the ICU.

Peeking through the threshold of Chaim's room, I spoke as loudly as I could. "Chaim, I feel so bad, but I have to go home for a few days to take care of the children."

From my vantage point I couldn't see him well enough to tell if he seemed to understand what I was saying or even if he heard me. It really was pointless to carry on this way.

"Sari, you can't be of any help here," Bina said. "Let's go to Tova's house so you can get into bed and rest."

"How can I turn Tova's guest room into a sick room?" I asked in consternation. "I feel terrible doing that."

"Sari, I assure you that Tova won't mind at all. I know her well."

I finally gave in to Bina's persuasion. "OK. I really do need to rest."

"I'll stay with you and sleep over at Tova's. Tomorrow I'll take you to the lab and then to the doctor." What an amazing friend Bina was!

"Sari, my dear," my mother-in-law said, "don't worry. We'll manage without you. I arranged for Maya, Binyamin, and Yanky to come and do shifts in the hospital."

Baruch Hashem for my extended family that was willing to share my burden. Ima's warm embrace and *refuah sheleimah* wishes expressed how relieved she was that I would now be able to get the rest I needed.

HOME SWEET HOME

The next phase of my life is something of a fog in my memory. I spent most of that time in and out of bed and it took me nearly a month to really feel better. Mother had arrived that Sunday night and I was very lucky to have her running the household with Bassy. But vacation time was coming to an end and Bassy had enrolled in a business course in Yerushalayim. She would soon be leaving us to live in a rented apartment with several friends. Mother decided she and Father would spend the *yamim tovim* in Eretz Yisrael with us. She was quite sure that we would sorely need their help.

Although I was ill, it was a joy to be back in my own home with my sweet children around. I hoped they hadn't suffered much while I was away, but there was really nothing I could have done about it. I had made a deal with Hashem that I would joyfully accept what He decreed for me because He knew best, and I intended to fulfill my part of the deal if I possibly could.

As strong as I was in my belief that "everything that Hashem does is for the best," I still felt very weak physically. It was due to Hashem's great kindness that my mother was with me, taking care of me as only a mother could.

One day she said, "Sari, I am so amazed at your fortitude and your resolve to remain calm with all that's going on! You're really amazing!"

I buried my head on her shoulder in response and hugged her. I was too overwrought to say anything. Her words were like salve on my aching heart. I never knew she thought of me in that way.

Meanwhile, my mother scoured the newspaper ads daily for a small apartment for rent during the *chagim*. She wanted to have her own place with Father once Chaim returned home. Happily, she found a two-and-a-half-room fully furnished apartment very close to ours for the month of *yom tov* with options for continued rental. She felt we would all be more comfortable that way. My father was due to come the week before Rosh Hashanah.

THE ENCOUNTER

During the three and a half weeks that I had spent at home, I was informed that Chaim had made great bounds in his healing. The brain swelling had completely resolved and the brain flap had been reattached. His memory was returning slowly but surely, and various brain exercises were a part of his daily routine. Additionally, he was doing physical therapy daily to regain the strength in his limbs. By the time I came to visit him, he was walking around with the aid of a walker. The doctors were talking about sending him home within the next week or so, just in time for Rosh Hashanah.

The day I returned to the hospital is deeply engraved in my memory. I came with my mother and Shoshi. We knew that Chaim would remember her because he had recognized her in the photographs that we'd shown him. I had never let anyone take Shoshi to visit her father while I was ill, as I felt she needed me by her side for such an overwhelming experience.

Both of us were very emotional, not having seen Chaim for so long. How would he respond to seeing us? Would he be able to express himself normally? I agonized over whether he had been upset with me for not being with him for so long. Did he understand that I was ill and not allowed to visit? Were the letters I sent him periodically a good enough substitute? Would he understand why his children hadn't come to visit him till now?

I won't be disappointed with a cool or indifferent reception, I thought, *even though the doctors warned me that this is a real possibility. Whichever way he'll respond is the best he can under the circumstances. I'm going to be happy with whatever he expresses.* I needed to impress upon myself that whatever we encountered was simply a step on the road that would lead to complete recovery.

I prepared Shoshi for our meeting. "Shoshi, because Abba hurt his head, he forgot how to do so many things that we do naturally, without thinking about it."

"What do you mean, Ima?"

"Well, it might be hard for Abba to kiss and hug you. He might not remember how old you are or that you're going to *gan chovah* very soon. With Hashem's help, over time, he'll relearn all of these things and become his regular self again. But we can't know how long it will take."

Shoshi was taken aback, but she quickly readjusted to the new situation.

"Shoshi, sweetheart," I continued, "if you sing one of Abba's favorite *zemiros* that you always sing at the Shabbos table, it will help him remember the old ways and remember you even better."

"But Ima, I'm ashamed to sing in front of strange people…"

"I'll send everyone out of the room," I promised, "and for the love of Abba you can sing just in front of me and him." She seemed OK with that idea and assured me eagerly that she would do so.

Chaim was now a patient in the neurology department of the hospital. He was in a physical therapy session when we arrived. We had to wait until he was returned to his bed before we could go in to him. Shoshi was getting a lot of attention from my mother and mother-in-law and was distracted, but I was impatiently sitting on the edge of my chair. The thirty minutes that we waited seemed like hours. Finally, we were permitted to enter the room.

My heart was beating rapidly as I clutched Shoshi's hand and walked toward the bed. Chaim was resting with closed eyes, tired after his workout.

"Chaim," I called softly. "I came with Shoshi to visit today. We are so excited to see you!"

He turned his head in our direction and opened his eyes. At first his eyes looked blank, but soon their expression changed to one of recognition.

"Is that you, Sari?" he said slowly. "Really you?" He seemed incredulous and happy.

"Yes, Chaim, it's me. I'm so sorry I couldn't be here when I was sick. Did they tell you I had an infection and couldn't come?"

He nodded his head.

"I'm all better now. How are you?"

"Good," he said simply.

"Here's Shoshi. She just couldn't wait to come to you!" I put her up close to the bed and she touched his hand. He looked at her and said nothing.

"Abba, how do you feel? I wanted to come such a long time ago, but no one could take me. Abba, Abba, I want you to come home already!" She kissed his hand and I noticed Chaim's eyes filming over.

He raised himself up and took her in his arms. He rocked her gently for a short while and then put her back down. It was hard for him to speak.

Finally, he said, "Shoshi, I'm happy you came. You're such a big girl. How old are you?"

"I'm five, Abba. I'm going to *gan chovah* after the summer."

"That's nice. What are you going to learn?" I could tell that he was working really hard at making conversation.

"To read *aleph-beis* and learn *Chumash* and add numbers and…I don't know. What do they teach children in *gan chovah*, Abba?"

"I don't know, Shoshi. But I'm sure you'll love it." He closed his eyes.

"Chaim, do you remember how beautifully Shoshi sings? Would you like her to sing something for you?"

I didn't want him to fall asleep yet. As long as Shoshi was here, I wanted her visit to stimulate his memory as much as possible.

"Sure," he said with his eyes still closed.

I signaled for my mother and mother-in-law to leave the room.

"OK, Shoshi, it's only us in the room. Now you can sing for Abba. You'll make him really happy, sweetheart," I encouraged her.

Shoshi put her heart and soul into her little performance that day. In her own childlike way, she understood why it was important for her father. The quality of her singing brought tears to my eyes. It wasn't long before Chaim opened his eyes to look at her. I could see the emotion welling up in them, but instead of crying, a big smile formed on his lips. He even clapped his hands in rhythm to her song.

When she finished, he asked for another one, and another one. I could see that he was exhausted from the exertion of listening and trying to remember and reacting with emotion. I said quietly, "I think that's enough singing for one day. Maybe you need to rest now, Chaim?"

Instantly, an annoyed look transformed his expression. "Why didn't you bring her here before?" he said harshly to me. "Can't you see how much I missed her? I don't need to rest. Why do you say I need to rest? You don't want me to enjoy myself? You go and rest!" He spat the words out angrily in a loud voice.

I was shocked! He sounded so agitated and irrational. I was hurt by his response. Instead of thanking me for bringing Shoshi, he was doing the exact opposite! I had to remind myself that he was displaying typical signs of someone having suffered brain injury. The doctor had explained that outbursts were one of many possible symptoms.

For Shoshi's sake, as well as my own, I put on a calm front and quickly said, "It's OK, Chaim, don't be upset. I know you love Shoshi and her singing, but the doctor said only a little bit each day. Too much of a good thing can end up being not so good. We're both so happy that the doctor let us come today. If you will rest now I'm sure he'll let us come tomorrow again and then you'll have some more singing. Right, Shoshi?"

"Right, Ima."

"Shoshi," I told her quietly, "tell Abba how much you love him and how much you want to sing for him another time." I hoped that if she spoke to him he would calm down and forget what he was angry about.

She did as I requested and luckily Chaim did calm down. If not, the doctors might have forbidden a subsequent visit. As it was, one of the doctors had entered the room having heard Chaim's raised voice.

"It's time to go," the doctor said authoritatively. Looking at me, he said almost accusingly, "He's exerted himself enough for today."

We said our goodbyes, but Chaim didn't respond at all. He didn't even look at us. I was afraid of what his indifference would do to Shoshi.

"Shoshi," I said quickly as we walked out, "Abba loves you very much but he is so tired now that he doesn't have strength to talk anymore and even to turn his head. But every day, *im yirtzeh Hashem*, he will get better and better until he'll be the same as he was before the accident."

"Poor Abba! I hope he gets better real fast." She seemed to accept my words at face value.

I had some niggling doubts about what I'd just said. Despite the hurt and disappointment in the way our visit had ended, I consciously determined to focus on my warning words to myself: *Whichever way he'll respond is the best he can under the circumstances. I need to understand that this is simply a step on the road that will lead to complete recovery.*

I knew in my heart of hearts that my self-talk was absolutely true. My higher self had no problem with coming up with all the *dan l'chaf zechus* excuses for his behavior under the circumstances. But that did not stop my lower self from crying for several hours that night before falling asleep. To say I was hurt was an understatement. I had been waiting so longingly for this meeting, for the sweetness of reconnection. My mind bombarded me with unanswered questions: *Why did it have to turn out as it did? How could he yell at us like that? And then ignore us as we left? Couldn't he muster up a quiet thank you or a semi-smile?* I was devastated!

My higher self argued with my lower self to no avail. And my tears broke down the floodgates of control and engulfed me in torrents. I had no choice but to let the emotions rage.

When I finally calmed down a bit, my higher self timidly spoke up and reminded me that ninety-five percent of our meeting had been very positive. It was so easy to lose perspective. I wanted to be all understanding, all forgiving, to be able to transcend normal human hurts and disappointments. I wasn't there yet. I now felt deeply worried about the effect Chaim's outbursts would have upon our marriage.

DISCHARGE FROM THE HOSPITAL

The happy day finally arrived when Chaim was discharged from the hospital, a few days before Rosh Hashanah. We were so grateful that he was well enough to go home for *yom tov.* He had been hospitalized for nearly six weeks. The staff made him a goodbye party with his doctors in attendance. I gave Dr. Tannenbaum a gift of appreciation for his dedicated care. He really deserved way more than my humble present, but at least it expressed my gratitude. I also brought a gift for Dr. Stern, the doctor presently in charge of Chaim's well-being.

Dr. Tannenbaum was no longer Chaim's caretaker. During the time I had been absent from the hospital he had been transferred from the Intensive Care Unit to the Neurology Ward. Dr. Stern, a neurosurgeon, had taken over Chaim's case. It was he who had decided that Chaim was well enough to go home and had ordered his discharge.

While the merrymaking was going on and everyone was eating my mother-in-law's delicious apple-cinnamon "farewell" cake, Dr. Stern approached. He wanted to speak to me and to anyone involved with Chaim's care in order to give us explicit instructions related to Chaim's continued healing.

I asked my parents and in-laws to come for a little conference with Dr. Stern. When we were all seated, he looked at us intently and, with a no-nonsense sounding voice, began speaking.

"Let me begin by saying that Chaim has had an amazing recovery. He could have been left with severe neurological problems and physical handicaps, but, thank G-d, this is not the case. He continues to suffer from numerous symptoms, but that is normal at this point of the healing process. However, his memory has almost completely returned and his physical and intellectual functions are nearly normal. I want to explain something about his medical condition and what you'll need to know for his future care.

"Chaim has suffered what we call a Traumatic Brain Injury or a TBI. Symptoms of a TBI can range from mild to severe and can last for hours, days, weeks, months or even years. These symptoms may include not thinking clearly or having trouble remembering new information; having headaches, vision problems, or dizziness; feeling sad, nervous, or becoming easily angered, as well as sleeping more or less than usual. There are many other symptoms that may appear and I will give you a list of them before you leave.

"As you recall, once Chaim's brain swelling and other signs of trauma resolved, we began treatment and rehabilitation, which may be necessary to continue on a long-term basis. I will give you a complete list of what treatments you'll need to continue with. These can help him feel more in control and help get him back to his regular life.

"I've written up some prescriptions to relieve symptoms of sleep problems, chronic pain, and headaches he's sure to experience. He'll need different medications if he starts to suffer from anxiety, depression, or memory problems. You'll need to talk with your local doctor or with me for a follow-up on his medications.

"Most people recover fully after a concussion. When we are dealing with adults with severe TBI, over fifty percent have a good recovery or only moderate disability. In adults with severe TBI, recovery occurs most rapidly within the initial six months. Smaller improvements continue for perhaps as long as several years.

"Rest is very important after a concussion because it helps the brain to heal. The injured person needs to be patient; healing takes time. Only when the symptoms have reduced significantly, in consultation with your local physician or with me, should Chaim slowly and gradually return to his daily activities. If his symptoms come back or he gets new symptoms, he should stop these activities and take more time to rest and recover. Ignoring symptoms and trying to 'tough it out' often makes symptoms worse. As the days go by, he can expect to gradually feel better."

"Is there anything else we need to be careful of?" I asked.

"Yes, of course. During the time he is healing, Chaim should be very careful to avoid doing anything that could cause a bump, blow, or jolt to the head or body. Sometimes, receiving another concussion before the brain has healed can result in many serious complications.

"I need to emphasize that the recovery time may vary. The monitoring of the patient's health is an ongoing process and you have to ensure that Chaim visits a doctor for frequent medical checkups.

"Here are two lists with important information." I looked down at the papers he had handed me, "Healing from a TBI" and "When to Call the Doctor."

The doctor scanned the group and continued. "This is a very complex situation and I stress the need to pay close attention to everything we've discussed today. In case of any questions or concerns you may have, I strongly encourage you to feel free to call me rather than waiting to see if things will improve. Any other questions?"

No one had any questions. We felt both uplifted by the miracles Chaim had experienced and also a little shaken by the possibility of remaining damage. I really appreciated that Dr. Stern had taken the time to explain everything in such great detail.

"One other thing I might mention," he continued. "In case you bring in a caretaker for Chaim, to bathe him or take him out for walks, and this is definitely advisable, as Chaim still suffers from bouts of dizziness, you must explain to them everything I have outlined to you today, especially the danger signs he'll need to be aware of. You may be entitled to receive the help of an aide due to Chaim's condition through your *kupat cholim* or Bituach Leumi."

Dr. Stern turned to me. "Mrs. Perlman, please set up an appointment with my secretary for a follow-up visit right after the Sukkos holiday." I nodded my approval.

"I wish Chaim a speedy *refuah sheleimah* and a good day to you all." We exited the room.

I felt exhilarated as Chaim walked slowly but steadily on his own two feet to the taxi that would bring him home. He was lightly supported by his father on one side and conversed naturally with all of us. His hair had grown in enough to hide the scars on his scalp and he appeared almost the same as the Chaim from before the accident.

CHAPTER THREE

Back Home

THE FIRST PHASE

I had no idea what life would be like with Chaim home. I discovered fairly soon that he would easily get angry at me, for no apparent reason. I tried to take it in stride by not thinking about it too much, as doing so would certainly cause me to lose sleep. One thing I knew was that I had to get *yom tov* ready. I thanked Hashem endlessly that my parents were in Eretz Yisrael to help.

I needed the two extra pairs of hands to deal with the cooking, shopping, and building the sukkah, since negotiating the medical bureaucracy was very time-consuming. I wanted to get the process started for registering Chaim for the various therapies Dr. Stern felt he needed. I also wished to apply for the services of an aide to help with the physical aspects of Chaim's care. That meant dealing with one of the departments of social services. Obtaining approval from them normally took quite some time. Since I had no idea how long my parents planned on staying in Eretz Yisrael, I felt compelled to obtain the necessary help for Chaim's care before I gave birth. As my due date was only three months off, I felt as though I were running a marathon, trying to outrun the moving hands on the clock of time.

To my great luck, the Reichmans were able to help again. Rabbi Reichman had connections in various government offices and was able to arrange my getting approval for an aide within a matter of two weeks. This was a real feat of *chessed*, as receiving such a quick response was almost unheard of. By the time Sukkos came, we were nearly set up with our new schedule. Alexander, the Russian aide, would take Chaim three times a week for his various therapies, as well as bathe him and take him for a walk every other day. The aide had been approved for a three-month period for five days a week, after which the office would make an assessment of the situation and decide whether to extend approval for another three months. Alexander's help was a true blessing.

ALEXANDER

Alexander was a middle-aged Russian Jew. After the Second World War, he and his wife had managed to escape the Soviet Union and settle in Rumania. Years later, through a circuitous route, they had landed on the shores of Israel. Right after Yom Kippur, he began working for us. A lovely, friendly person, he was always smiling and making others feel good. The funny stories and jokes that he told his "patients" reflected his natural talent for lifting people's spirits.

Alexander didn't know much about Yiddishkeit but was very open to learning more about his heritage and religion. It was lucky that he spoke Yiddish because he didn't speak a very good Hebrew. I spoke Yiddish quite well. Chaim had picked up Yiddish while living in the United States, and surprisingly his recall of the language was good despite his difficulty with memory in other areas. And so, between the two languages, he was able to communicate fairly well with Alexander.

Chaim immediately undertook to teach his new friend the rudiments of being Jewish. Teaching Alexander acted as a stimulus to his memory by slowly bringing to mind the myriad details of what being an observant Jew was all about. I could see that it made him feel really good to be back in his role of *kiruv*. They made a wonderful pair, the two of them helping each other with their individual needs.

THERAPY

The therapy schedule was rigorous and time-consuming. When he was home, Chaim slept a lot. I was happy that the therapy kept Chaim so busy. Since he was constantly focused on regaining his health, he did not have lots of free time to think about his misfortunes. His day was full and pleasant as a result of Alexander's delightful nature. *Baruch Hashem*, he was making wonderful progress.

It took about a month after we returned home for Chaim to be able to walk to shul with Alexander on the days he came to work for us. Chaim had regained his ability to daven and was using some of his free time to teach Alexander to read *lashon hakodesh*. Alexander himself was excited, like a little cheder boy, to learn the art of praying from a siddur. Chaim was slowly becoming the skilled teacher that he had once been.

The thing that seemed to bother Chaim most was loud noises and the squabbling of the children. He'd get irritable, irrational, and would often shout at them. My parents were still with us and they took the children out to the playground as often as they could. But I knew that Chaim would have to get used to noise, as before long, there would be a crying infant in the house and in his bedroom.

I discussed the noise issue with Dr. Stern, asking if there was a way to alleviate the problem.

"A colleague of mine from Sweden has established a hearing clinic based on his studies in Vibroacoustic Sound Therapy," he replied.

"Professor Isaksson has invested his lifeblood and all of his assets in developing this clinic. It is quite unique in Israel, still experimental, but he's had some wonderful results, especially when dealing with trauma. He uses a unique sound room as the main part of the therapy."

The Isaksson Sound Clinic sounded impressive, but being treated meant going to Tel Aviv twice a week. Could we fit it in to Chaim's already overloaded schedule? I decided to leave the decision up to him.

One day, after a particularly volatile outburst, I broached the subject.

"It looks like the children's noise really bothers you," I mentioned gently.

"Of course it does!" He literally spat the words out. "It feels like someone is rubbing steel wool inside my head!"

"Oh, how awful!" I was shocked at this brutal description of his. He had never expressed his feelings or talked about what he was suffering prior to that moment.

"It must be really hard to deal with, Chaim. I never knew how badly it made you feel."

"How could you possibly know," he said simply. "No one can know what I feel."

"Chaim, Dr. Stern told me that there's a sound clinic in Tel Aviv that does therapy for hearing problems. Do you think you might want to check out their program? It means schlepping to Tel Aviv, but maybe it's worth it."

"Maybe it's worth it," he repeated in a daze. "Maybe it is."

I wasn't sure if that meant that he wanted to go or even if he understood what I had told him.

"Should I make an appointment for you?" I asked.

"Only if you come with me," he replied. "I don't want to go there with Alexander."

He sounded like a child asking his mommy to come with him to an unfamiliar place, a place that frightened him.

"Sure, Chaim. I'll be very happy to come with you."

I figured that if he felt that the clinic was helping him he would want to continue there and I would eventually be able to give the job of accompanying him to Alexander. But going to Tel Aviv would have to be at the expense of one of his other activities. The only one I could see removing from his schedule was the short daily *chavrusa* session he had with Rabbi Reichman. That would be a big pity, as it was the only Torah learning Chaim did. But what could we do? The noise issue was taking its toll on all of us, as Chaim's irritable outbursts often made the children cry. And, I had to admit, me as well. Rabbi Reichman would surely understand!

I was racing against the clock and so the next day I immediately got to work on setting up a plan. I called Rabbi Reichman.

"Hello, Rabbi Reichman. It's Sari Perlman."

"How are you?"

"Fine, *baruch Hashem*? And how are you?"

"*Baruch Hashem*. How can I help you today?"

"Dr. Stern recommended that Chaim be treated in a sound clinic for his hearing sensitivity."

"That sounds interesting."

"Yes, it does. The problem is that we have to go to Tel Aviv twice a week for appointments and I can't figure out how to fit that into our schedule. It seems like we don't have enough hours in the day for everything that needs to be done."

I hesitated for a moment before continuing. I certainly didn't want to offend our loyal friend and mentor who'd helped us in so many different ways.

"The only thing I found to cut out of his busy schedule is his learning *chavrusa* with you, of course only temporarily until we finish the program at the hearing clinic."

"No, no, no! That's impossible!" was his immediate reaction. "I'm quite sure that in the *zechus* of Chaim's learning, he will see progress in his healing at an unusually quick pace. Yet I quite understand your predicament. Give me some time and I'll figure out a way for the learning session to continue daily."

The creative rabbi came up with a plan that demonstrated his *mesiras nefesh* for Torah and for his close friend Chaim.

He called back that evening. "Here's my plan. If you could arrange the hour of the clinic visits to coincide with my lunch break from yeshiva, I'll travel with you to Tel Aviv and Chaim and I can have our *chavrusa* during the ride. Then, at the clinic I'll use the time to prepare for the next day's *shiur* and on the ride back, I'll try to catch my 'forty winks.'"

"That's an amazing plan, Rabbi Reichman! I'm really impressed. I'll do my best to make the appointments fit your schedule."

"Believe me, I wouldn't do this for just anyone, but I want Chaim to know how significant his every effort expended for learning Torah is. And I want you to know that you're not allowed to compromise Chaim's Torah learning in any way, if it is at all possible. Of course, Chaim has to agree to the plan. I'll speak to him as soon as I can."

I immediately made the necessary calls to the hearing clinic to enable the plan to evolve. And Rabbi Reichman set into motion obtaining Chaim's approval for the new learning routine.

THE SOUND CLINIC

It took some doing but we finally got our plan underway. I came along that first day, as I'd assured Chaim I would. Alexander joined us too. I wanted him to be familiar with the layout of the clinic. I was hoping that for the next visit, Chaim would agree to Alexander accompanying him instead of me.

We took a family-size taxi to Tel Aviv. Alexander sat next to the driver, the *chavrusa* partners sat in the middle row so that they could learn comfortably, while I sat in the back. However, Chaim appeared unexcited and rather passive. He had a hard time focusing on the Gemara lesson. The change of locale, the noise from traffic, the movement of the car, in addition to the extra people around must have been too much for him to adjust to. But the good rabbi was not discouraged.

I spent the time saying *Tehillim*. There was so much to pray for. Each new therapy we undertook was another form of *hishtadlus* toward Chaim's healing, but we knew that the Ultimate Healer had to give His approval for the therapy to accomplish its goal. I prayed that the *Rofei Kol Basar* would be with us on our trip to the hearing clinic.

Most people I'd spoken to had never heard of it and were skeptical as to its efficacy. I was skeptical too, but eager to try it out. If Chaim could adjust to the noise in his environment and react normally to it, I would be eternally grateful. If he didn't adjust soon, our home would become a torture for him with the addition of a new baby's crying night and day and a torture chamber for us too with the outbursts those cries would evoke from Chaim.

We got to our destination in record time, as the traffic was quiet during the lunch hour. Within a matter of minutes, we entered the clinic office. I was given a form to fill out and Chaim answered some questions the secretary asked him. The next step was entering the mysterious "Sound Room."

"Mr. Perlman, ideally you should be alone in the sound room," the secretary said, "but in light of your condition, you may prefer being accompanied by someone."

"Yes, I do." Chaim often spoke very briefly, as speech was still sometimes an effort for him.

"Whom do you wish to accompany you?" she asked.

"My wife."

I expected this response, but I wanted Alexander to join us.

"Chaim," I spoke up quickly, "would you mind if Alexander came along too?"

"OK." He must have realized that I would not accompany him for much longer and had to make peace with the fact that Alexander would be his companion at the clinic in the future.

A man then joined us in the office. He was a pleasant-looking fellow with a big smile.

"Good afternoon. My name is Ayal Gordon and I'll be working with Chaim for the duration of the time he spends here. I'm called a desensitization therapist. My work entails desensitizing the patient to sounds that cause him distress. You may be surprised to hear that various forms of sound therapy have been in use since the last century.

"I'm sure you're curious about what takes place in the Sound Room. I'll give you a short explanation now and you can read a more detailed one in the booklet we have prepared for our clients. After the session, you can ask any questions you may have or discuss your concerns with us.

"Chaim is suffering from a condition called hyperacusis caused by his head injury. Hyperacusis is a critical condition of health when any kind of sound, or certain sounds, become intolerable to hear by the affected person. Generally, the sound that irritates the hyperacusis patients never creates any trouble to normal people. Sound Retraining Therapy is the most popular and common therapy for hyperacusis. This treatment requires listening to noise, called 'pink noise,' just below the patient's intolerance level. The noise generator helps to maintain a balanced level of noise in the background. After listening to 'pink noise' at a soft level for a stipulated period of time, the patient can rebuild his or her tolerance to sound. Eventually, it leads to normal environmental sounds no longer causing discomfort or pain. It's a long procedure, and with the support from family and friends, a patient can be on the road to recovery in about six months.

"Today we'll start with a short 'sound' session. Over time, we'll build up to longer ones. If all goes well and Chaim responds favorably, after a number of sessions, you will be able to continue the therapy at home with a rented sound generator.

"Do you have any questions?"

"What do we do while we're in the room with Chaim? Can we talk to him?" I asked.

"You can talk to him and he can talk to you. However, we prefer that he focus on the sound that is generated in the room. In order to protect you from that sound you'll be given headphones, and that will make it difficult for you to hear him speaking. Preferably, you can spend the time reading or knitting, or on any other silent activity. The same goes for Chaim himself.

"Only once we see that Chaim has adjusted to the therapy and is responding positively will we recommend commencing the therapy at home. So ideally, you would keep the talking to a minimum, if at all."

I nodded in understanding.

"If there are no other questions, let's get started." Ayal stood up and we followed him into the sound room. Alexander and I were given headphones to wear. As soon as they were in place, I noticed that a red light on the wall lit up and I understood that the noise generator had been turned on. The pink noise was now filling the room.

"Today we'll do twenty minutes unless Chaim exhibits distress. We will observe him through the one-way window and will hear whatever he says though our special microphone system. In the event that he expresses discomfort, we'll cut the session short." Ayal left us and closed the heavily padded door.

We sat down on a double settee. "Well, Chaim, what do you say about this room? It's nice, no?" I spoke louder than usual as I wanted to be sure Chaim heard me.

"I don't like the color pink!" he replied sharply.

I was taken aback by his answer. There was so much to look at beside the generous splashes of pinks and purples in the furnishings. There were nice pictures on the wall, as well as rocking horses and other interesting toys.

"Chaim, what color do you like?" I asked.

"I like blue. I like brown. I like black. Not these stupid baby colors."

Maybe it wasn't even a color issue. Maybe he mentioned the color pink because subconsciously he was worrying about the "pink noise."

Or, I wondered, could it be that the noise he was being exposed to was bothering him. I couldn't hear it because of the headphones and even if I had heard it, it probably wouldn't have been an issue for me. So I had to be sensitive to what he was going through.

"Is the sound bothering you?" I asked with real concern.

Chaim grimaced. "It's not too bad. It's a bit irritating but no big deal really. I think I just feel uncomfortable that I have to be here at all. It makes me think about all my difficulties since the accident."

The tears sprang unbidden to my eyes. This was the first time Chaim had expressed himself in this way. I was glad he had told me what was going on in his mind.

"Chaim," I said genuinely, "I'm really proud of you for never complaining about anything, for never being bitter or showing a lack of *bitachon*. You're amazing that you can accept what Hashem's sent you!" I paused, because I wanted the words to sink in. He appeared touched by my expression of pride in him.

"Let's make this a fun time together," I continued, "and before you know it, we won't have to come here anymore. You'll keep on improving until your noise problem is gone."

I wasn't sure if I was shouting because the earphones made it hard for me to hear Chaim and that automatically made me raise my voice. But Chaim wasn't wincing from the elevated decibels emanating from my throat, so I continued.

"Is there anything you would like to do?"

Chaim sat quietly as he thought about my question. He finally said, "I'd like to play chess."

I laughed out loud. I couldn't believe he would want to do something that took so much concentration and focus. It sounded wonderful but not very realistic. Did he even remember the moves?

"Chaim, I'm not a very good chess player. I don't even know if I remember all the moves. Maybe we could play checkers instead. It's easier so we'd have time to finish it before we have to leave. Do you want to play checkers?"

He didn't answer right away. I think he really wanted to see if he could actually play a game of chess. That would be some accomplishment for him if he could swing it. I assumed that Alexander played chess since I figured that all Russians did. If so, now he'd get the additional job of building up Chaim's skill at chess.

Chaim seemed lost in thought. I wondered if the pink noise was distracting him, or even confusing him. I decided to take down the checkers game from the shelf and set it up. If Chaim wanted to play he would. If not, not.

I looked at my watch. Only six minutes had passed since we'd entered the room. Twenty minutes seemed much longer than it had sounded. I pulled a small table over to where he was sitting and set up the checkers board. I then found a lightweight chair and positioned it opposite Chaim. I sat down and observed him. He looked at the board and made no move to play. I couldn't tell if he knew what to do, or just couldn't decide if he wanted to play or not. I let him take his time deciding.

He just sat there silently looking at the board. My heart started pounding unnaturally as the tension slowly built up inside. After about three minutes of staring mutely at the game in front of him, he finally made the first move. I felt like shouting for joy, but restrained myself. I played the next move. And that's how we started playing checkers after not having played for years. I felt like a young girl again.

The red light on the wall opposite me went out and the door opened. Ayal walked in and came over to us. His perpetual smile was in place as he put his hand on Chaim's shoulder.

"Good job!" he said enthusiastically. "You were great! Some of our patients fidget and walk around or even call for us to come and take them out of the room. But you were a model patient. Maybe your game of checkers helped out too."

Chaim smiled shyly in response to the compliment. I collected the checker pieces and placed them in their box with the board.

"Thank you, Ayal, for this most interesting experience," I said as I returned the game to the shelf. "I'm not sure about Chaim, but I thoroughly enjoyed myself here." I was exaggerating for Chaim's sake. I wanted him to remember today's visit positively.

"What about you, Alexander? Did you like being here?" I wanted to compound the positive feedback about this place as much as possible.

"Loved it!" he said. "If I can play with little toy soldiers again that will be good. But I love to play checkers too."

I had a feeling that Alexander was smart enough to understand the importance of making this room sound like the most desirable place in the world to be in.

Ayal took our headphones that we had removed from our heads.

Rabbi Reichman had managed to finish preparing his *shiur* and was pleased that he had this opportunity of uninterrupted quiet in which to do it. After a short debriefing with Ayal and taking care of payment, we started on our way back to B'nei Brak.

Our next appointment was in three days' time. I told Alexander that I wanted him to join us, although I intended to be there as well to be sure that Chaim was comfortable and willing to go. I hoped it wouldn't take long until Chaim was able to go with Alexander alone. My excursion meant that my mother had to take care of the children on her own while I was away and that I missed my afternoon nap which, in my condition, I really needed. But if Chaim would actually become desensitized to noise, then what I was doing was the smallest sacrifice I could make for him. I only hoped that we could get to the point of home treatments before the baby was due.

The next session was clearly more problematic than the first. It might have been because the volume of the pink noise was increased, causing Chaim to respond poorly.

We started our checkers game and I sensed Chaim's irritability increasing moment by moment. After about ten moves he suddenly yelled, "This is such a stupid game. Why would anyone play this ridiculous game?!"

With a violent sweep of his arm he turned over the checker board and the pieces went flying in all directions. He got off his chair and started pacing the room like a caged animal. I was shocked into silence. I noticed that the red light went out and almost simultaneously the door opened.

Ayal had stopped the treatment and walked in.

"Come, Chaim," he said quietly. "Come with me." He led us into one of the therapists' offices and introduced us to Dr. Flora Neuman.

"Please, sit down Chaim. Don't be alarmed by what happened," the therapist said in a quiet voice. Chaim made no eye contact with her and seemed to be looking at the floor.

"What happened to you could have happened to anyone else being treated here. We have no failures with our treatments, only feedback. Your reaction tells us that we increased the pink noise too much."

Chaim seemed to relax somewhat and actually raised his head to look at her. Encouraged by his response, she continued speaking.

"In light of your recent injury we now realize the need to go at a slower pace, more suited to your level of sensitivity." Chaim nodded his head slightly.

"We were so encouraged by how well you did the first time that we mistakenly became a little too enthusiastic. You know, sometimes too much of a good thing is not good at all. But rest assured, we won't repeat the same mistake again."

I wasn't at all sure if Chaim comprehended everything she was saying, but her voice was so soothing that I could literally see him unwinding. His shoulders dropped about an inch and his fists unclenched. He leaned back more comfortably in the chair and his facial features softened. Relief swept over me for I believed that now Chaim would be ready to continue the sound sessions.

The therapist smiled encouragingly. "Do you have any questions, Chaim?"

"Not right now."

"Good. I think Ayal would like to speak to you."

"Chaim, how about helping me pick up the checkers pieces and putting them away." Chaim, as a father and teacher, was all too aware of the need for neatness and order, and so could not easily refuse Ayal's request.

They returned to the sound room and Ayal was careful to leave the door wide open as they walked in. He had Chaim do several tasks there while the sound generator was obviously turned off. The idea was to get him to feel comfortable in the room once again so that he would be willing to enter it next time he came.

"You know, Chaim, the damage to your brain made you more sensitive than I realized. Trust me that I'll be working with you at a much slower pace than normal."

They said their farewells and we made our way home.

During the entire trip, Rabbi Reichman spoke quietly to Chaim, encouraging him to continue the sound therapy. He explained how often we go through *yeridah l'tzorech aliyah*[9] — a regression in order to advance, to move upward. He continued speaking and eventually convinced Chaim to continue therapy. I knew that I would have to accompany him for the next few sessions until I was sure that all was going well.

It took five more sessions before I felt that Alexander could take over for me. I was relieved that Chaim was progressing according to the reports Ayal gave us. He always came home from his sessions tired and slept afterward.

Chaim's progress was slow but steady. His hearing sensitivities were less acute, but he still had a long way to go in the sound room. Our big question was, when could we continue therapy at home? The baby was due any day now.

CHAPTER FOUR

Resuming Normal Life

THE NEW ARRIVAL

For as long as I can remember, life for me had been classified as either before the accident or after. The two lives were so different from each other.

With no warning, we were suddenly thrown into the role of supporting and helping our Chaim, my children's father. We had been such a happy, relaxed family, doing so well in all areas of our life. Suddenly, day turned to night. The frightening question was always present in my mind: Would we be able to extricate him from the dark abyss?

After months of daily struggle, my body could no longer cope with the added burden, knowing that it had to conserve its energy for the coming of the new addition to our family. I was afraid that I would not be able to carry on in my active role for even one more day.

I felt stretched to the limit. It's strange, though, how we really don't know what our limits are. I needed to learn that one can always stretch a little more, even if it's a minuscule amount, beyond what we call our comfort zone. Hashem helps us grow by stretching us bit by tiny bit, especially when we least want to.

I was in the kitchen, cooking and listening to a new tape of Chassidic music that Mother had bought me, when Chaim walked in. I was surprised, as I thought he was walking outside with Alexander. They must have cut their outing short as it had started drizzling.

"What's that ridiculous music you're listening to?" he said angrily. The music was very lively, with drums and trumpets, and I would never have turned it on had I known he was home.

"It's called 'Keitzad Merakdim' by the Simcha Boys Choir." My tone was very matter of fact, but inside my stomach was knotting. I felt relieved that the children were out shopping with my mother.

"Get rid of it right away!" he yelled. "Don't you know that I can't bear it?! It's horrible, horrible, horrible! Don't you understand anything?"

He violently pulled the plug out of the wall socket and the tape recorder crashed to the floor. "You never do anything right anymore! You're awful, you're just out to hurt me!!" He slammed the kitchen door shut as he ran out.

My whole body was trembling. I could not hold back the tears that coursed down my cheeks like a winter rain. Suddenly the room felt cold and dark, as though menacing clouds had descended upon it. "I understand, Hashem, I understand," I whispered. "You never abandon me, no matter what. But why does it have to hurt so much?"

What would be? Could our marriage survive? I decided to call Rebbetzin Scheinerman and share my burden with her. Her warmth and empathy diffused my suffering and strengthened my resolve to keep doing whatever had to be done, no matter how long it took.

Just in time, Hashem orchestrated events so that the sound sessions could continue at home. At the same time, we got authorization for a three-month extension of Alexander's services for three days a week. Happily, my mother decided to stay on for another few weeks.

I wisely prepared an alternate bedroom for Chaim, normally our guest room, as I did not want to subject him to a newborn's only way of expressing his needs — by crying out. I knew that sometimes that cry would pierce the heavens in its desperation, a common practice with newborns. For Chaim, that would be a torture I could not allow him to endure. My fervent prayers were that Hashem should grant us a healthy baby and that He would give me the strength to cope with the needs of both infant, invalid, and, of course, myself. Hashem, in His limitless goodness, did just that.

CHANUKAH

It was Chanukah once again. I loved those little lights twinkling so brightly in the windows and on the porches surrounding us on all sides. They were tiny messengers of hope in a dark and difficult world. They let us know that we were always connected to the spiritual world from where Hashem was watching and protecting us. Chanukah always made me feel safe and uplifted.

I had such fond memories of the Chanukah two years prior, walking to the car in the snow in my slipper-clad feet. On that night, the sixth Chanukah light, our little Yochanan made his debut into the world.

This year, to our great delight and good fortune, we hosted Alexander and his wife, Irena, for Shabbos Chanukah. Alexander was so excited to light Chanukah candles for the first time in his life, and the couple enjoyed themselves thoroughly. *Motzaei Shabbos*, after lighting the fifth Chanukah light, Alexander and Irena played dreidel with Chaim and the children, while my mother discreetly took me to the hospital. That night we were blessed with our second son, Yaakov.

THE SECOND PHASE

Mother would have wanted to stay on indefinitely, but that wasn't possible. Father had left shortly after Sukkos and Mother planned on returning home once Yaakov turned a month old. As a present for the birth, my parents were paying Alexander to come to work for us three days a week, in addition to the three days the social services paid for. They also promised that they would pay for Alexander to continue coming three days a week once the government stopped doing so, and for Irena to do housecleaning twice a week. That was a very generous present for my middle-income parents. Oh, how I wished they could always be nearby, so that we could enjoy their dear company and not only their monetary goodness.

Another wonderful thing that Mother did for us was to persuade Alexander and Irena to move into the apartment she had found for herself and Father once she went back home. In this way, the elderly couple that had grown so close to us, and had grown in their Yiddishkeit as a result, would be nearby to help out if needed. It was a brilliant idea!

Despite Chaim's progress with his hearing sensitivity, Yaakov's crying was still very irritating to him. During the day, we sent Chaim out with Alexander as much as was feasible. He also spent two hours daily wearing special headphones that connected him to the sound generator that we had rented. During that time, he read, learned Torah, or played chess with Alexander.

MOTHER GOES HOME

I could see that Mother's heart was torn in two as we said our goodbyes at the airport. We all accompanied her, including Chaim with his earplugs in place. Alexander and Irena came along too, as they were beginning to feel like a part of the family.

The children couldn't understand why she was leaving.

"Why are you going away, Bubby?" Shoshi lamented as she held on tightly to her grandmother's hand.

"I have to take care of Zeidy, my darling. We'll come back for Pesach, OK?"

"Pesach? That's so far away!"

"We can't wait that long." Miri joined Shoshi in her protest.

Yochanan continued to suck his thumb. Luckily, Yaakov kept quiet, as he was asleep in his baby sling.

"Children," I said, "Bubby was super-duper for staying this long and leaving Zeidy to take care of himself. I want you all now to tell her thank you for being such a good Bubby!"

What a sweet chorus of "Thank you, Bubby!" rose up from their throats. It caused some heads to turn, as well as a few tears to be shed. This was indeed a difficult moment for us all.

Chaim thanked Mother for all her help in a most heartfelt way. It was gratifying to me to see him responding to this emotional situation maturely and with sensitivity. This was real progress on his part, as expressing his emotions had been quite difficult for him. Mother realized this, as well, and I could see how moved she was.

We exchanged our final farewells and hugs. The moment came to part and in an instant Mother was gone. I heaved a sigh as I kissed the top of Yaakov's head, trying to fill the emptiness I felt with the love of my baby.

CHAIM BEGINS TEACHING AGAIN

As much as I could work it out, l saw to it that Chaim wasn't around Yaakov when he was crying. However, I often gave him the sleeping baby to hold. I didn't want him to be completely disconnected from his son, and this was a good way to rouse his love for his child. Chaim began learning Mishnayos out loud when holding Yaakov. Sometimes the baby awoke and listened quietly to his father's voice with his eyes focused intently on the face above him. I think that did a world of good for Chaim's fragile self-esteem.

Since the accident, Chaim had been transformed into someone quite different from the man he had previously been. Many times, he didn't know who he was and what he was capable of doing. Instead of being the teacher, the leader, the decision-maker, he had become someone who didn't know what was happening and was completely dependent on others. Becoming his old self meant taking painstakingly slow steps to relearn doing the things he had done in the past without any conscious effort; doing the things he loved to do, and regaining his old personality.

Teaching Alexander to read Hebrew had been a wonderful beginning for Chaim. At some point, he began teaching Alexander and Irena about Jewish law. This meant that he had to first study the halachah inside the *Kitzur Shulchan Aruch*, and then work out how he would explain it to the elderly couple in a way that was understandable to them. This required a major output of energy that he wasn't always capable of. But when he did give them a lesson and he successfully taught them something new, he was ecstatically happy. It gave him a tremendous feeling of accomplishment. It reminded him of who he really was.

Now that he was holding Yaakov and acting as though he were teaching him Mishnayos, it aroused within him the longing to once again teach others the holy words of Torah. Yaakov, named for our forefather who represents the Jew who sits in the tents of Torah, would be the catalyst for Chaim to begin once again teaching Torah.

CHAIM'S FIRST CLASS

Every time I observed Chaim "teaching" his baby son Mishnayos, I realized how important it was for him to become the scholar and teacher that he had once been. I spoke to Rabbi Reichman about it, wondering if he had any ideas for how Chaim could begin teaching again. He said he would try to figure something out.

It didn't take long before he came up with an idea. Often, newcomers to yeshiva needed some extra help with their studies. Some of the boys didn't even read Hebrew fluently when they first arrived, let alone understand Aramaic. Two of these boys were really struggling with the new languages. Without a basic grasp of *lashon hakodesh* and Aramaic, they could never advance in their learning. Rabbi Reichman asked Chaim if he was willing to tutor the boys twice a week, for pay, of course. He readily agreed.

The first time Mike and Joe came for their lesson, I sent the children to play at the neighbors. I knew how much doing this meant to Chaim and didn't want anything to interfere with his concentration. There was a lot at stake here and I sincerely prayed for Heavenly help. I even baked a chocolate cake and made freshly squeezed lemonade, as I wanted Chaim to know that I was celebrating his new position in life.

The boys and Chaim hit it off from the start. The conversation and the learning were lively and Chaim was greatly invigorated by the encounter. I was thrilled by how a simple forty-five-minute tutoring session could so greatly enhance his self-esteem.

Before the boys left I served them cake and drinks. As they dug in, Joe commented, "Thanks, Mrs. Perlman. Nothing beats homemade chocolate cake!"

Mike added his own few words of praise as I walked them to the door. Things were looking good, and I was sure they would only get better and better from now on.

I BEGIN TEACHING

Chaim continued tutoring once or twice a week and blossomed as a result of his efforts. Although Rabbi Reichman paid him, the income was minimal. We were receiving a monthly sum from Bituach Leumi, the Israel National Insurance Institute, as Chaim was considered handicapped and was unable to work. However, the amount was not nearly enough for the needs of our growing family. I decided that as soon as possible I would begin working to bolster our meager income. Yaakov was a good baby and I could get a neighbor's daughter to be with the children while I took a few hours off to earn something.

I spoke a fair Hebrew but I wasn't sure if I could manage teaching Lamaze with the vocabulary I possessed. I would have loved to give classes in English, but there was an American in town by the name of Merry Sherman who was already doing that. Both of us could not teach Lamaze in English.

My Hebrew was adequate for normal conversation, but for child-birth classes I needed to know how to teach anatomy and physiology. Understandably, my language skills were not on that level. So I bought some books on childbirth in Hebrew and constructed a vocabulary list from them. Once I felt sufficiently prepared, the next step was to advertise myself.

Before long, I put together my first class of four women. I covered our *sefarim* closets with sheets and turned the dining room into our classroom. After buying some exercise mats and a few books for a lending library, and digging up my teaching aids from the boxes in storage, I began my Hebrew-speaking Lamaze career.

Hashem was good to me, and despite my natural shyness and feelings of insecurity with my language skills, He helped me succeed wonderfully. I started off small, but slowly my reputation grew, as well as the size of the classes. Eventually I had to move out of the house and rent a studio. I taught in the evenings, no more than twice a week, and was a full-time mother for my children up until bedtime on those days. Sometimes they weren't quite asleep by the time I had to leave the house. They would stand on the porch and wave to me as I walked off to work. I always asked them to daven for me that I should have a successful class, and they complied happily. I was careful to hire a babysitter that they liked and so things worked out nicely.

Once I got used to working part time, I decided to reintroduce photography into my life. My beloved hobby had provided me with a lucrative income while living in Lakewood. I unearthed my tripod, other photography tools, and decorative wall hangings from the boxes in storage. I used my studio by day to do portrait photography, and before long, created a name for myself in this field as well.

THE THIRD PHASE

Although all concerned were pleased with Chaim's progress, there was something that troubled me about his condition. On rare occasions, for no apparent reason, Chaim would react with extreme anger or perhaps, one might say, fear. His reaction was always disproportionate to what was going on at the time. He could scream and yell words that seemed disconnected from his surroundings. He might turn over the children's games and on occasion hit them. Sometimes he even broke things by forcefully throwing them across the room. On more than one occasion, he threw the children's toys down from the porch to the ground below. Sometimes, he would insult me and yell at me for no plausible reason. Always, after his outburst, he became extremely exhausted and would fall into bed and sleep for several hours. When I would try to discuss what had happened with him later on, he seemed not to remember much or else he denied that the event had even taken place. He never questioned his behavior or tried to figure it out. Rather, he seemed to be trying to suppress the memory of those unsavory moments.

Dr. Stern told me that this was normal for people who had undergone TBIs and one could never know when and if all symptoms would disappear. Since Chaim's outbursts were considered "normal" according to medical criteria he could not authorize another brain scan. However, if the pattern of these episodes changed in any way, I was definitely to be in touch with him, and he would reevaluate Chaim's condition. The one piece of practical advice Dr. Stern gave me was that I would have to act as a detective to try and figure out what triggered Chaim's outbursts.

CHAPTER FIVE

The Yom Kippur War

A PUBLIC THANKSGIVING

Summer vacation was upon us and my hands were full with the children out of *gan*. We were approaching the first anniversary of the accident. Thinking about it brought up painful memories. Although Chaim had come a very long way in his healing during this time, he was far from complete recovery. He still tired easily, was sensitive to certain types of noise and sounds, and sometimes had angry outbursts. On the whole, though, we were very happy to see Chaim functioning at the level he had attained.

One day, I got a phone call from the yeshiva.

"Hello, Mrs. Perlman. Rabbi Reichman here."

"Hello, Rabbi. How are you?"

"*Baruch Hashem*, fine. Let me get to the point. I thought that it would be a good idea for you and Chaim to make a *seudas hoda'ah*, a thanksgiving feast, on the date of the accident. It would be your way of thanking Hashem for the fact that Chaim survived his ordeal and has made such an amazing recovery."

"Um, I don't know," I murmured hesitatingly. "Wouldn't Chaim feel self-conscious with all the attention drawn to him?" I wanted to reject the idea.

"I don't think so. I believe he'd actually relish the opportunity."

As the idea sank in, I realized that we did need to express our thanks to Hashem publicly for all the *chasadim* He had done for us.

"You know what? Why don't you speak to Chaim about it," I said, "and see how he reacts. If he approves of the idea we'll go ahead, and if he doesn't there's really not much we can do about it."

I was surprised when Chaim readily agreed that we should make the *seudas hoda'ah*. I never realized that he felt so strongly about his recovery. When we talked about it together he let me know that he realized that he could easily have been left in a vegetative state due to the severity of the brain injury. I found out later that he had been reading the pamphlets that he had taken home from the hospital discussing brain injury and had even borrowed some layman's books from the doctors he had become friendly with. It seemed he knew more about his condition than I did.

Together with Rabbi Reichman, we worked out a plan. Normally, the *yeshivos* have *bein hazemanim*, a three-week break between Tishah b'Av and the first day of the month of Elul. This year, however, Rabbi Reichman had decided to initiate an optional *yeshivas bein hazemanim* — a summer learning program. Over twenty boys had signed up. Rabbi Reichman created a timetable for them to complete learning *Mishnayos Shabbos* by the date of the accident. The yeshiva's *siyum* would be celebrated with the Perlman family's *seudas hoda'ah* and we'd share the expenses. This plan made things so easy for me, as all I had to do was shop and Chaim would bring the items over by taxi. The yeshiva cook would prepare the food and the boys at Shaarei Orah would set up and serve. Rabbi Reichman arranged for a *mechitzah* to be erected in the dining room so that women could attend as well. He also hired a small music band to accompany the singing and dancing.

The one remaining thing for Chaim to do was prepare a speech expressing his thanks to Hashem for all the miracles he had experienced. He wanted to give the boys an inspirational message to take away from the event and spent weeks preparing, as he delved into our holy *sefarim*. Painstakingly, he created a moving *d'var Torah* and a declaration of praise and thanks to the Almighty.

The day finally arrived. The celebration was scheduled to take place after *tefillas Minchah* in the yeshiva building, and the feast would serve as our midday meal. The children and I were dressed in Shabbos clothing for the occasion. The excitement in the air was palpable, although the little ones didn't quite understand what was happening.

Shoshi needed to understand. "Ima, tell me again why we're dressed up in Shabbos clothing and eating lunch in the yeshiva."

I spoke to all the children as I answered her. "Do you remember what happened last summer on this very day?" I asked them. They looked at me with wide-open eyes.

"On this day last year, the 17th of Av, Abba went on a trip with the boys and fell in the wadi. He hit his head on the rocks and was taken to the hospital. Some people who hurt their heads so badly don't get better. But Abba did get better and we want to thank Hashem for giving him a *refuah sheleimah*. So we are making a special *seudah*, a feast to thank Hashem in front of all the people in the yeshiva and the people we invited to share our happiness with us. We want to show Hashem how grateful we are for all the good He does for us. And at the same time, the yeshiva is making a *siyum* for finishing learning *Mishnayos Shabbos,* so we are celebrating for two reasons. And that's why we're going to have a special delicious meal and sing and dance with music."

"It's like Simchas Torah!" Miri piped up.

"No!" Yochanan was already talking like a big boy, although he had a limited vocabulary. "It's a party. I want chocolate!"

"OK, sweetheart, you'll get some chocolate or ice cream. But first you must eat your meal like a good boy."

We arrived at Yeshivas Shaarei Orah in time for *tefillas Minchah*. After that, everyone filed into the yeshiva dining room. The hall was full of our invited guests. My in-laws came for the celebration with some of Chaim's siblings. Bassy was there to share our joy with us, literally feeling a part of our family. Bina and her children came, as well as Merry Sherman, and other close friends. Obviously, Irena and Alexander attended, very much excited for us. I was really moved by the show of love and happiness they all expressed.

The dining room, festive with colorful streamers, was decorated with a big handmade sign that read: "*Ivdu es Hashem b'simchah* — Serve Hashem with joy."[10] The tables were tastefully set with table-cloths that matched the paper goods that I had selected. Our mouths watered at the sight of the buffet, laden with a colorful display of delicious dishes.

Before the meal could begin, the actual *siyum*, completion, had to take place. Rabbi Reichman chanted the last words of the Mishnah and thereby completed the learning of that particular section of the Oral Torah. Afterward, he gave a short speech expressing his joy and pride in his Shaarei Orah boys for the Torah learning they did.

Then it was time for Chaim's *d'var Torah* and thanksgiving speech. I uttered a sincere prayer for his success. I needn't have worried. He delivered his words flawlessly and with passion. His message was quite moving.

One thing he said that impressed me greatly was related to the date of the accident.

"You all know that today, the date of the accident, is the 17th of Av. The word *tov*, meaning good, has the numerical value of seventeen. Do not be fooled by this seeming coincidence. Nothing in life is a coincidence. Hashem has sent a hidden message for me and for all those who were involved with my accident. I have come to believe that what happened to me on that day was truly for the good, as is everything that happens to all of us. All the pain and suffering and effort expended with my healing are serving some positive purpose, although I may not know exactly what it is. Surely someday I will understand the benefit in everything that I have undergone.

"But even now, as a result of my accident, I feel increased appreciation for every function and ability that the Almighty has granted me. For that alone it was worth going through the suffering and the painstaking efforts at rehabilitation that the accident has caused. I sincerely hope that I will never revert to taking things for granted and always maintain this level of gratitude to Hashem."

It was hard not to cry, and many of us did.

The speeches were over and I became the center of attention on the ladies' side of the *mechitzah*. Bassy insisted on holding Yaakov so I would be free to interact with my friends and relatives undisturbed. It felt strange being given this much attention, but it was a great feeling knowing why it was all taking place.

People were moving off to wash their hands for the meal. I was standing near the *mechitzah*, with Bassy holding Yaakov next to me, when I heard a familiar voice. Mike appeared at the edge of the partition and said to Bassy, "Mrs. Perlman, I wanted to wish you—" He stopped in embarrassment as he realized that the lady holding the baby was not Mrs. Perlman. He stood there in silence for a moment, looking into the unfamiliar face, but quickly collected himself.

"Sorry! Excuse me. I was looking for Mrs. Perlman."

My brain took a mental photo of the two of them standing next to each other and filed it away for a later time. I quickly stepped over and said, "Hello, Mike! I'm so glad to share this wonderful occasion with you. After all, you are part of what made Rabbi Perlman the success he is today."

"Oh no, Mrs. Perlman, Rabbi Perlman is part of what made me the yeshiva *bochur* I am today!"

"Sorry I didn't bring any home-baked chocolate cake for you on this grand occasion!" We laughed together, remembering those far-off days when Chaim had just returned to teaching.

"As I was saying," Mike continued, "I wanted to wish you much ongoing *nachas* in all that your husband is doing. And also that he should have a complete recovery, quickly, and help more young men like me become the best they can become."

"Thank you, Mike! Thank you. I wish you much success in your Torah learning and in your future life. It's really nice to see you again."

He returned to the men's side and Bassy and I went to wash hands for the meal.

The meal was great and the music and dancing were amazing. The children had a wonderful time, with presents and lots of attention from everyone. We came home exhausted but very happy. It was truly a memorable event.

THE SHIDDUCH

The mental photo I had taken of Mike and Bassy returned to my consciousness with a rush the day after I took it. They seemed so perfect together. It didn't take much persuasion on my part to convince Bassy to go out with Mike. And Mike didn't need much convincing either. He trusted that since we thought Bassy was a suitable prospect for him the *shidduch* was a good idea. And it didn't take much time before the two of them became engaged to each other. It was a match made in heaven!

I was so excited! It was the first *shidduch* that I'd ever made! Mike wanted to live in B'nei Brak as Rabbi Reichman had a learning program for married men. Bassy had a job in Yerushalayim, but her company had a branch in Petach Tikva and they promised to transfer her there. So living in B'nei Brak was perfect for her as well. It was good news for us both, as this way we could continue our friendship and mutual help to each other in the years to come. They planned to get married right after Sukkos.

A NEW YEAR BEGINS

Rosh Hashanah came and went with many tears of supplication and much inspiration. After the *seudah mafsekes*, the last meal before the Yom Kippur fast, Irena and I lit candles. The adults left for shul while I stayed home with the children. I promised to tell them a very special story if they would play quietly and keep Yaakov happy while I davened *Ma'ariv*. They were so compliant and sweet that I spent a long hour telling them about all the miracles that took place in the Beis Hamikdash on Yom Kippur.

During the break between *tefillas Shacharis* and *Mussaf*, Chaim and I were resting in the bedroom when we were suddenly terrified; sirens began to blare. We had no idea what they meant, and I didn't know how to comfort the frightened children and my agitated husband. Before we could decide what to do, the all-clear signal sounded. We looked out from the porch to the street below. Was it possible? On the holiest day of the year we could see jeeps rushing through the streets in a town that never allowed traffic on the Sabbath. There were soldiers in uniform walking on foot, probably still fasting...to where? Before long we heard jets flying through the air to some far-off destination. Was this war?

Chaim was thoroughly shaken and became uncontrollably agitated. He didn't throw things, but he paced the room back and forth like he had so many times before. He reminded me of a caged animal. He yelled things that really didn't make sense and managed to frighten the children and myself quite a bit. He carried on for a good fifteen minutes, while I talked to him quietly and calmly. I kept on assuring him that all the *tefillos* of our great nation on this very special holy day would ensure our safety and survival. By consistently repeating my calming words, I managed to restore him to a balanced state. He did not excuse his behavior, but claimed that he was tired and went to bed to sleep.

Was it the air-raid siren that created such a negative response in him? How many more such sirens would we be subjected to if we were in the midst of war? I felt at a loss to deal with the situation.

Chaim was sleeping deeply and I felt the need to plead for salvation in shul where the prayers carried more weight. The opportunity to do so came our way unexpectedly with Irena knocking at our door, frightened to be home alone.

Once I calmed her down I broached the question, "Irena, would you mind watching the children while I go to daven *Ne'ilah* in shul?"

"Sure, Sari. You go, I take care of children."

The specially prepared bags of treats were taken from the pantry and given to the little ones. They would keep them busy while I was gone.

Our shul was about a fifteen-minute walk from the house and I got there just in time for the start of the *tefillas Ne'ilah*, the fifth prayer of the day. The sun would soon set and the Heavenly gates of prayer would then be locked. This was our last opportunity on this holy day to implore Hashem for all that we needed and desired.

I davened with deep concentration. My prayers were accompanied by copious tears, for our safety and the safety of all of Am Yisrael. I davened for Chaim's continued and complete healing, for our family's well-being and whatever else I could think of in the moment.

As I finished the silent *Shemoneh Esrei* prayer I felt a sense of peace settling down deep within myself, for I knew Hashem had heard every word of my supplications. But then, ruthlessly, in one moment, that peace was shattered as the air-raid siren blasted its mournful wail throughout the skies. "Danger! Danger!" it seemed to be telling us with cruel finality.

My heart began beating relentlessly as I rushed down the stairs from the ladies' section and into the street. Although I was weak from the fast, I ran through the streets along with other women and children, all trying to get home as quickly as possible.

My poor babies must be frightened out of their wits, I thought. I blamed myself for leaving them for shul, rather than forgoing my prayers in order to be with them. I had no idea if a missile was speeding toward us or not, but an air-raid siren was terrifying to hear! I felt great relief as the all-clear signal was sounded during my run, still before I got home.

I made it to the house in record time with my heart pounding furiously. A most amazing sight met my eyes. All of the occupants of our apartment house were standing in front of the bomb shelter on the ground level of the building. Mothers with babies in arms and small children who were too young to be in *shul*, including Irena with my children, had converged in front of the shelter. However, since it was full to bursting with everyone's baby carriages, playpens, folding beds, sukkah walls, bamboo bundles, broken chairs, and old washing machines, the shelter was sheltering the "junk" instead of the occupants of the house. I would have burst out laughing at the irony had the situation not been so frightening.

I ran over to my precious little ones. "Ima! Ima!" they cried as they hugged me tightly. Yaakov promptly began screaming hysterically the second he saw me. I scooped him into my arms and pressed him close to my heart.

"Thank you so much, Irena," I said warmly to our extremely shaken-up babysitter. "Thank you for taking the children down to the shelter. You must be so frightened!"

"Yes, Sari, I am. But I so happy to be here with you and not home alone."

"Irena, be my guest and spend the night with us. We'll make room in the living room for you and Alexander."

She relaxed visibly upon hearing my offer. Together, we walked up the three flights of stairs to our apartment. I wondered if Chaim was still sleeping or if, *chas v'shalom*, he was having another attack. To my great relief, he was still asleep. Maybe this was his subconscious way of protecting himself.

Once Yom Kippur was over, we listened to the radio to find out the gruesome news. Over the following days, we discovered just how devastating our casualties were, mostly young men in their upper teens or early twenties. Many had been burned alive in their tanks!

Eretz Yisrael was indeed the proverbial lone lamb among the seventy ravenous wolves. How would we survive this ordeal?

THE ELEVENTH OF TISHREI

The night after the fast, we were shaken to the core again as the air-raid sirens blared. Chaim, poor soul, was hysterical. It was clearly the sirens that were triggering him. I had no choice but to use the sleeping pills and tranquilizers that I had at home for him as I had no way of getting in touch with Dr. Stern. We were at war now and Dr. Stern would probably be on call day and night treating the wounded. I would have to act as Chaim's doctor for the time being.

That night, once Chaim fell asleep and the house was quiet, I wrote a letter home to my parents. I couldn't call them, as it was still *yom tov* in America. But I had a need to talk about my experience, express my fears and concerns, and connect with my parents, to whom I felt so close. The letter was seven folio pages long and I mailed it the next day.

The sun dawned on a strange scene in our town. The streets were overflowing with broken furniture, rusty bicycles, and odds and ends of junk that had occupied everyone's bomb shelters. The sukkah walls and bamboo bundles that had been stored in them were leaning against the walls of the buildings or lying in the yards. Every building had a committee to assure that the bomb shelters were emptied out and fit for use. We had no idea how long this war would last and how often we would need to use our shelters.

The war casualties were heavy and the fighting was fierce, both in and around the Suez Canal, the Sinai Peninsula, and in Syria. As a result, sukkahs were going up rapidly in every home as many of the men from neighboring families belonged in the reservist units of the army and were expecting to be called up at any moment. Tension ran high.

SUKKOS

The holiday of Sukkos arrived and Chaim's parents and unmarried siblings were spending it with us. The children doubled up in their beds to make enough room for the women not sleeping in the sukkah.

It was difficult to feel the words of the song, *"V'samachta b'chage-cha* — and you shall rejoice in your holidays,"[11] the traditional *yom tov zemer,* and a commandment in the Torah, but my father-in-law did a good job at trying. Chaim was on a tranquilizer, per instructions of Dr. Stern whom I had luckily been able to contact by phone. The entire family, as well as Chaim, benefited because one of its effects was that the air-raid sirens were now less traumatic for him. We would have to deal with the underlying cause of his anxiety once the war was over.

POST WAR

The war was over in just under three weeks and everyone tried to get back to normal. Thank G-d that the nearly three hundred Israeli hostages were released through a prisoner exchange within a few months of the end of the war. But there were countless families shattered by the loss of their husbands, brothers, and sons. Our nation had lost two-and-a-half thousand precious souls, most of them youngsters, barely having tasted life.

The whole nation was sobered by the fact that Israel had been caught unaware when the conflict erupted. Had those in authority heeded the signs of activity on the opposite side of the Suez Canal and the warnings of the Israel Defense Forces (IDF) Directorate of Military Intelligence, the death toll would have been dramatically reduced. It was a decree from Heaven that the indications of impending war had been ignored.

Ever since the brilliant and amazing victory of the Six Day War in 1967, the IDF had become inflated with pride and ego. By all that had happened in the present war, Hashem was letting the Israeli heads of state and military know, "No, it is not you who wins the wars. There is a Higher Power that you have forgotten about that brings victory or defeat." Many came to the realization that had Hashem not fought our battles for us, we would certainly have been wiped off the face of the map. *"Hinei lo yanum v'lo yishan Shomer Yisrael —* Behold the Guardian of Israel does not sleep nor does He slumber."[12]

MIKE AND BASSY'S WEDDING

Bassy was desperately trying to get ready for her wedding. Now that the war was over and I felt safe leaving the house, I spent hours shopping with her and helping her set up her apartment.

"It's so good of you, Sari, to spend all this time with me!" Bassy's eyes shone with gratitude. "How would I ever have managed without you?"

"You have no idea, Bassy, how much I am enjoying helping you get ready for your wedding. You're practically part of our family, and there's nothing I would rather do than this!"

I bought material to sew dresses for myself and the girls. Simultaneously, I planned and began preparing a *sheva berachos* for the new couple. The pressures of my life felt overwhelming, but I knew that with Hashem's help I would get everything done on time.

Bassy's and Mike's parents and three siblings were coming from the States for the wedding and we had to find a place for them during their stay

The day finally came and by a miracle we managed to get everything ready. Bassy got dressed and made up for the wedding in our home. She was a real princess! The women accompanied me and the children to the wedding hall in a minivan, while the two fathers and brothers went with Chaim to bring Mike to the wedding hall. Shoshi and Miri got the coveted job of holding the wedding-gown train as Bassy walked regally into the hall.

The night passed in a glow of happiness and dancing. To me, it felt almost as though I was marrying off a daughter. I came to realize how true the words were that "giving is receiving." The giving I had done these past few weeks paled in comparison to the magnitude of what I was now receiving. Joy, *nachas*, satisfaction, and fulfillment were the benefits, to name a few, of the *chessed* we had done for Bassy as her adoptive family. Mike, too, felt indebted to us for all we had done, and in recognition of that he gave Chaim a *berachah* under the *chuppah*.

CHAPTER SIX

In Quest of Healing

THE APPOINTMENT

The war was over, the wedding was over, and my mind was drawn back to the issue we had temporarily put aside — Chaim's attacks triggered by the air-raid sirens and his recurring sensitivity to noise. At the first opportunity, I scheduled an appointment with Dr. Stern.

The doctor was happy to see us again. I noticed that he looked quite a bit older, even weary, since we had last seen him. He must have been under great strain during the war, with the heavy load of injured to treat. I realized that we were lucky to have gotten this appointment after only a few weeks of waiting. He was probably treating all of his old patients as well as the injured soldiers that were still under his care.

He studied Chaim's file carefully, along with the progress report we brought from Ayal.

"I'm pleased to read that you are progressing steadily with your sound sensitivity issue," Dr. Stern said. "It seems you're still having attacks triggered by loud noises. Can you tell me more about these attacks, Chaim? Can you tell me what you feel just prior to the onset of the attack?"

Chaim was silent for several seconds. Then he simply answered, "No. I'm not aware of what I feel."

"Are you aware of your thoughts just before or during the attack?"

"No."

"Can you describe what happens as you are going through it?" the doctor wanted to know.

"I really can't remember much of anything about it."

"That's all right, Chaim. It's quite possible for people to be unaware of what's going on when they have certain types of attacks. But it's important for me to know how it presents in order for me to understand it and to treat it."

The doctor then turned to me. "Mrs. Perlman, please help me out. Tell me what you remember about an attack, as if you were describing a movie of it that you had just watched."

I felt uncomfortable telling the doctor what Chaim's attacks looked like, as though I was speaking *lashon hara* about him. But I realized that for him to be treated, I had to describe as carefully as I could all the details of Chaim's strange behavior. I collected my thoughts.

"Well, they are not all the same," I began, "but certain aspects always reoccur. For example, after hearing the loud noise, which can vary in pitch and intensity, Chaim's mood immediately changes. He becomes very tense, maybe anxious is a better word, and angry. He will yell or even scream loudly and angrily at the children or myself, or other people on occasion. Sometimes, he'll say things that aren't even related to what's going on, things that are irrational. He might pace back and forth. Sometimes he throws things; sometimes he throws the children's toys down from the porch of our third-floor apartment. Sometimes, he even hits the children, never very hard but enough to frighten them badly. Sometimes he'll slam the door and run away from wherever he was to the bedroom and throw himself into bed. He usually sleeps after an attack for a few hours and never talks about it afterward. I wonder if he even remembers what he just went through."

As I talked, I sneaked a look at Chaim from the corner of my eye. He seemed to disconnect, as though he wasn't there in the room with us.

Dr. Stern took note of Chaim's behavior and body language as he listened to the account of the attacks that he suffered and had no recollection of. The doctor asked him to do certain exercises in order to assess his neurological function. He then attached several electrodes to his scalp and observed his brain activity while asking him questions. He could see that talking about the attacks created anxiety for Chaim in a specific area of the brain. After removing the electrodes, he recorded his findings and then turned to us.

"I'm happy to see the great improvements you have made, Chaim, since last examining you. On the one hand, you've made fine progress toward regaining normal function. On the other hand, I can see that there is still some source of irritation triggering your attacks. The electrodes I attached to the various parts of your head show me that when you think about your attacks, the part of the brain that is stimulated is the area where you store memories. It seems that when a certain traumatic memory is activated it triggers an attack.

"It's possible that your subconscious mind has repressed the memory because it doesn't want you to have to deal with it any more. Your subconscious mind does this to protect you from being subjected to experiencing the pain of it again. Does this make sense to you?"

Chaim nodded his head but asked no questions. I, however, needed to know more.

"How can we deal with a situation in which the subconscious mind does not give us access to the memory of it?" I asked.

"Good question, Mrs. Perlman. Sometimes we don't actually need to access the memory in order to neutralize its negative effects. And there are a number of ways to do that. But sometimes it is preferable to access the memory, and we can do that through hypnosis. Doing so would give us a better way of dealing with it and neutralizing it completely."

"But I thought you couldn't make someone do what they are opposed to doing under hypnosis. And so if the subconscious mind doesn't want us to access the memory, how could hypnosis make it happen?"

"You're right about not being able to force someone under hypnosis to do what he is truly opposed to doing. For example, you couldn't make someone kill another person if he didn't want to, just because you commanded him to do so under hypnosis. But what we can do in certain situations is to cause the subconscious mind to change its opinion about something. So if previously it felt that it was 'dangerous' for Chaim to access a certain memory, under hypnosis we can help it to understand that it would be to Chaim's advantage to access it and to effectively deal with it. The subconscious mind will be willing to change its decisions about things if it trusts the hypnotist, if it feels assured that he is doing everything to help Chaim. If the subconscious mind felt uncomfortable or did not trust the good intentions of the hypnotist, we probably wouldn't get very far in creating change."

"I'd recommend that we schedule Chaim for a computerized tomography scan in order to get a clearer picture of what's going on in the brain. There may be some underlying cause of his attacks, like the formation of an abscess or a new bleed. My feeling is that it is related to memory, but I have to rule out any other possibilities. Once I have the results of the scan I'll make my diagnosis and protocol for continued treatment."

He looked directly at Chaim, "Is this clear? Do you have any questions?"

Chaim looked at him blankly, silently. Finally he said, "No."

"Chaim," Dr. Stern spoke kindly yet firmly, "would you like to get rid of these attacks?"

It took a few moments, but then he answered, "Yes, of course! It's very upsetting to lose control and hurt those around me."

"Do you have any fears related to the treatments?"

"I'm not sure. I don't know what you'll be doing to me…I think that I trust your decision about my treatments." Chaim began to relax. It was good that he was able to express himself.

"Well, I'm certainly glad to hear that. I do want you to ask any questions you may have about what we are doing to treat you. It's your mind and your health and if you have any concerns I want you to express them. OK?"

"Thank you for being so understanding, Dr. Stern. Yes, of course. Thank you." Chaim suddenly began to look like his old intelligent self again.

Dr. Stern smiled at Chaim's response; I could see that he really cared about him.

"Chaim, I'm going to start you on a new tranquilizer called Meprobamate that might be more effective than the one you are presently taking," he said while filling out the form for the CT scan and the various prescription drugs we needed. "I want you to call me after a week or two and let me know how the tranquilizer is affecting you and if you're noticing any adverse side effects." He handed Chaim the forms. "Please make an appointment with me once you've done the scan."

Just before we left Chaim suddenly asked a question. "Dr. Stern, how close am I to being totally healed?"

The doctor fingered his letter opener and took his time answering. "That's a little hard to say, Chaim, before I see the results of the scan. There may or may not be some unresolved damage there. And on the other hand, your brain might look completely normal in the scans but you may still be experiencing changes in your behavior and irregular reactions to things. As a rough guess I'd say that you're seventy-five to eighty percent healed. But I can't say how quickly or slowly the remaining twenty to twenty-five percent will take. I think you should be quite pleased that you've gotten this far."

"But it's more than a year already." Chaim sounded surprised.

"There are never any guarantees with this type of brain injury. In some cases, there isn't complete healing. If your function in daily life is satisfactory, that is something to be very grateful for."

We said our goodbyes and left. I could tell that Chaim felt as apprehensive as I did about what lay ahead. We made our way silently to the Central Bus Station for our trip back to B'nei Brak. Then Chaim said something totally uncharacteristic of the person he had become since the accident. "It'll be OK, Sari. I know, *b'siyata d'Shmaya*, it will be OK." I felt as though a bit of the old Chaim was being restored to me at that moment.

We could only get an appointment for the CT scan for a few weeks later, but Chaim started the new drug immediately. At first, the tranquilizer seemed to have deeper, calming effect on him. We were encouraged by the apparent positive changes. But suddenly, from one day to the next, Chaim started feeling lightheaded and couldn't concentrate. Once he nearly blacked out. He also had sleep disturbances and bouts of anxiety. Upon speaking to Dr. Stern, he told Chaim to immediately discontinue the drug and go back to taking the old one.

"I'm sorry, Chaim," Dr. Stern said. "I was hoping that Meprobamate would help. It's a relatively new drug and we still don't have a lot of data on it. We'll just have to be patient and see what to do after I see the results of your CT scan."

POST COMPUTERIZED TOMOGRAPHY

We returned to Dr. Stern with the results of the scan just as soon as we could get another appointment. He'd guessed correctly that there were no physical reasons causing the attacks, and that they were most likely triggered by a traumatic memory. He discussed the pros and cons of treatment with psychotherapy and hypnotherapy. Chaim and I agreed that we would get quicker results using hypnotherapy. Chaim was anxious to begin as soon as possible.

Dr. Stern gave us a list of certified hypnotherapists practicing in Israel. There weren't many, and even fewer close enough to our home. We also had no way to know who the best one was.

"We'll do a little research and take our time deciding how to proceed," I told the doctor.

"Please get these medications, Chaim," said Dr. Stern, "and be sure to take them regularly as instructed. I'd like to see you again in six weeks."

He quickly filled out the prescriptions and handed them to us.

"Good luck finding a capable practitioner."

"Thank you, Dr. Stern. We'll be in touch with you once we begin therapy."

Immediately upon arriving home, we turned to the *rav* with our query. Rav Scheinerman advised us to go to a hypnotist who'd been in practice for a long time and who could give us references. He told us that, most importantly, he should be experienced in dealing with trauma. We found someone in Ra'anana who had been doing hypnosis for more than eighteen years and had dealt extensively with trauma, particularly with soldiers who had fought in various wars. The Association of Israeli Veterans gave him an excellent recommendation. So we scheduled an appointment with Dr. Phillip Aarons. Luckily for us, Ra'anana was only a twenty-minute drive away by taxi.

Dr. Aarons, born to Israeli parents, had grown up in South Africa, and to our good fortune, he spoke both English and Hebrew fluently. He was a clinical psychologist as well as a hypnotist and had had a busy practice before making aliyah to Israel thirteen years earlier. In our first phone conversation, we explained that we were interested in dealing with Chaim's trauma via hypnosis rather than psychotherapy.

"I practice client-centered therapy, which means I do my utmost to comply with the desires of my patients. But my psychological background will only help to serve you, as the mind is a very complicated machine."

A bit confused by what he was saying, we nevertheless decided to give him a try.

"I would like Chaim to stop taking the tranquilizers so that I can obtain an accurate picture of what he is feeling," Dr. Aarons suggested. "I will also be better able to study the triggers causing his attacks without the tranquilizers obscuring what's really going on."

"We'll check with his doctor and get back to you," I replied.

Chaim called Dr. Stern himself and received approval to come off the meds. He then set up an appointment with Dr. Aarons for the following month, allowing enough time to wean himself slowly from the tranquilizers. I was thrilled to see that Chaim was once again taking responsibility for his well-being.

I was very interested in learning more about hypnosis before we started. I found several English books on the subject and began my education.

I was fascinated by what I read. The hypnotist brings the patient into a relaxed state by speaking in a special way that induces calm, like the soothing tone one might use when trying to lull a child to sleep. However, a state of hypnosis is not a sleep state. The patient can often hear what's going on, like the ringing of a phone, but experience it as an unimportant background sound. This happens because the subject is focused much more intensely on the words of the hypnotist and on his own internal state rather than on stimuli from the outside world. The person might stop reacting in a logical manner to what is being said or implied; rather than "thinking," he might begin to feel and experience, like one does in a dream. If the hypnotist would suggest that a cool wind was blowing on his face the patient may literally feel it. Physiologically, his brain waves would change from Beta, which dominate our normal waking state, to

Theta or Alpha, which occur in a relaxed or daydreamy state. In this "altered state of consciousness" the hypnotist can then access the subconscious mind of his patient and enable therapy to take place. And that is why he is called a "hypnotherapist."

Some of the case studies described in the books I read amazed me. A skilled practitioner could bring about dramatic changes in a person's feelings, perceptions, and even behaviors. He could strengthen his client's immune system or numb his pain. He could enable him to remember forgotten incidents or to change his perceptions of the past. He could make him feel disgusted by his beloved cigarettes or make him break out in a rash as he imagines touching poison ivy. If very skilled, he could even train a patient to undergo surgery without anesthesia, and feel no pain.

Still, a hypnotist was not a magician. He wasn't always successful in attaining his goals or in creating long-term change. If, for example, the patient was resistant to being hypnotized or unwilling to follow the hypnotist's suggestions, the hypnosis would be ineffective or the changes would not be long-lasting. What would happen with Chaim?

TRYING HYPNOSIS

Impatiently, we counted the days and finally the longed-for date arrived. We set out for the appointment with hope in our heart.

The secretary, Dalya, gave us a form to fill out and shortly after we entered the doctor's office. He wore gold-rimmed glasses, was tall and slim, and had a small knitted *kippah* on his head. His smile was broad as he stretched out his hand to shake Chaim's. I noticed that his handshake was firm and he impressed me as being sure of himself.

"Please, make yourselves comfortable," he said with a very distinct South African accent. We both sat down as he opened a folder on the desk in front of him. The window to the left of my seat faced a lovely tree-lined park. The splashing sounds of a water fountain floated through the window on a gentle breeze. It added to the calm

I felt in this office. I nearly forgot the serious nature of the reason for our visit.

"Can I please have your doctor's referral papers and summary of the case?" I was jolted out of my reverie as I handed over the medical files I had brought along. It took Dr. Aarons several minutes to read through them. He looked up and turned to Chaim.

"Would you like me to address you as Mr. Perlman or as Chaim?" he asked.

"Chaim."

"Call me Phil or Dr. Aarons, whichever you prefer."

"I'll decide when I get to know you better and see what feels right to me," Chaim replied.

"No problem. We always go at your pace.

"Tell me, Chaim," he continued, "how do you spend your day?"

Chaim took a few moments to organize his thoughts. He looked slightly uncomfortable. "I rise at seven a.m. to go pray in shul. After I come home, I eat breakfast and go to the yeshiva where I teach for two or three hours. If I have a good day, I spend more time in yeshiva and pray *Minchah* there. If I feel tired, I go home earlier. I eat lunch with the children, if it works out, and spend time doing homework with them. Then I go to rest.

"In the afternoon I do my physical therapy exercises, walk outside, and prepare my lessons for the next day of teaching. I swim in a local pool twice a week in the evening. This helps strengthen certain areas of my body that were injured in the accident. In general, I try to get to bed by eleven. Sometimes I get so tired, I need to go to bed much earlier."

Dr. Aarons was scribbling notes quickly in Chaim's file. He looked up and nodded approvingly. "That sounds like a very wonderful and productive day. So what brings you to me, my friend?"

I knew that the doctor had read in the medical report what Chaim's complaints were. From the hypnosis books, I knew that hypnotists always like to hear from the clients what they feel the problem is. The hypnotists themselves are very careful to avoid using the word "problem" in the interview, or ask them "what's wrong?" They don't want to call the issue "a sickness" and they try to be as positive as possible. I enjoyed hearing how Dr. Aarons was asking for the relevant information.

Chaim looked even more uncomfortable than before. He hesitated before answering.

"I sometimes get these attacks that I can't control. I feel very exhausted afterward and usually go to sleep for a few hours."

Dr. Aarons asked quite matter-of-factly, "Can you describe these attacks to me?"

"No, I can't. I can't remember much about them other than seeing the children frightened and crying, and a worried look on my wife's face."

"Chaim, I'd like you to close your eyes and try to remember. What do you do or say? How do you feel during an attack?"

Chaim closed his eyes and I could see him working hard at trying to remember. His brow was furrowed and his face was tense. He took several minutes before opening his eyes and answering.

"I sometimes scream. I sometimes throw things. I pace back and forth."

"Very good, Chaim, that you were able to remember all that. Now, try to feel the feelings that you experience at that time. Close your eyes and go back to the memory."

It was clear to me that Chaim was very uncomfortable with what was happening. As he was trying to bring up his feelings I could see the beads of perspiration that broke out on his forehead. I myself was beginning to feel uncomfortable. I wanted to protect my husband from his anxiety.

Chaim's eyes suddenly popped open. "No!" he almost barked. "I don't know what the feelings are!"

Dr. Aarons' expression remained calm and pleasant. His face held on to its seemingly invincible smile. "That's fine, Chaim. There's no need for the feelings to come up. You're doing just fine." He filled a cup of water and handed it to him. "Here, have a drink. It'll make you feel better."

Chaim made a *berachah* out loud and drank the whole glass in a few swallows. He put the glass down on the desk and sat there silently.

"Chaim, I'd like you to come over to this comfortable chair. In this special chair, special things happen. Come. Make yourself comfortable. You can open the footrest if you'd like." He waited until Chaim settled himself.

"Would you like your wife to stay in the room during the session or would you prefer she wait in the waiting room?"

"I want her here," he answered immediately. Once again, I could tell that he felt uncomfortable. There was obvious resistance in Chaim to accessing his feelings. I prayed that the session would go well.

"No problem, Chaim. She can stay in the room the entire time. Do you have any questions about hypnosis?"

"What are you going to do?" he asked very brusquely.

"I'm simply going to speak to you in a way that will make you feel calm and relaxed. You might feel like you are going to sleep or you might feel alert. You may feel as though you are sinking down or like you're floating upward. However you feel is fine. There are no rights and wrongs in hypnosis."

"So how will you heal the attacks?"

"As you enter this altered state of consciousness I will speak to the other part of your mind that knows more about you than you do about yourself. That part of you can do a lot of healing. For example, do you know how the immune system works?"

"No," Chaim answered simply. He sounded more relaxed.

"Do you know how you digest your food? Or how you make your heart pump blood? Or how you regulate your blood pressure? Or how you make your hormones work?"

"No."

"So which part of you knows how to do all that?" He paused for effect. "There must be another part of you that knows how to do all those things. That part of you we call the subconscious mind. It also holds all of your memories from the moment you were conceived and maybe even before that. That's the part of the mind I am going to talk to. It has an amazing ability to heal you."

"Can't it refuse to do what you ask it to do?" Chaim's question dealt with the crux of the issue of whether hypnosis would work or not. I was curious to hear the doctor's answer.

"Well, Chaim, that can happen sometimes. Occasionally it takes time until the subconscious mind trusts what is happening, but once it realizes that what is taking place is in your best interest it will cooperate with us. Does that make sense to you?"

Chaim did not look convinced. "Are you saying that the subconscious mind can think and make decisions about whether or not it likes what you are doing?"

"In a way, yes. All I have to do is show the subconscious mind that everything I'm doing is for your benefit. If it doesn't trust me, it will not go along with me. No matter what happens, you will always remain safe."

Chaim nodded his head.

"Are you ready to begin?"

"What if I don't like what you're doing?"

"Chaim, you will be in control the whole time. You'll simply tell me that you don't like what I'm doing and I'll choose a different method to achieve the goal. You'll always be able to express yourself if you wish to say something. If you wish to get up and leave, you will be able to do so as well. I work with you and for you and never, G-d forbid, against you. Even if you were completely hypnotized and a fire alarm were to go off in the building, you would be aware of it and jump out of the chair and run out of the building. You have a safety mechanism inside of you that will protect you at all times. Does this make sense?"

"I guess so," Chaim said. "But I still have one more question. What if the subconscious mind doesn't trust you at first? How long will it take to get to trust you?"

Dr. Aarons chuckled quietly at his query. "Well, Chaim, that really depends on how cautious this subconscious mind of yours is. But I would take a guess that by the second or third session I will be able to gain its full confidence."

"OK. Let's start." Chaim leaned back in the recliner. Dr. Aarons turned on soft, relaxing music at a low volume, dimmed the lights, and began the session.

"Take a deep, slow breath," the doctor intoned, "and let it out sloooowly."

He waited for a few seconds before continuing. "That's right; very good...Now continue taking those nice, deep, slow, relaxing breaths...at your own pace in your own way...Very good...." His voice had changed into a soft, soothing tone.

"And as you continue taking those nice, deep, relaxing breaths, you begin noticing that your entire body is relaxing...just giving yourself permission to let go...just being in the moment...not thinking about the past or worrying about the future...Just being here in the moment...." The doctor paused as he watched Chaim taking another few breaths.

"That's right. Very good! Just allow yourself to go deeper and deeper."

Chaim was complying with the doctor's instructions, despite his occasional fidgeting.

"And now, just let your eyes close gently, and feel yourself sinking down into the chair." His voice was low, monotonous, and truly hypnotic. Chaim noticeably sunk down deeper into the upholstery. His head fell slightly forward.

"And as you continue breathing, you become more and more comfortable...and as you become more and more comfortable your body becomes heavier and heavier...As your body becomes heavier and heavier you notice your eyelids becoming heavier and heavier...That's right...Those eyelids become so heavy that you just don't feel like using them...you don't feel like making them work...They feel so comfortable just as they are...almost as though they were glued together...So heavy, so comfortable...."

Suddenly Dr. Aarons began speaking very quickly, bypassing the conscious mind and speaking directly to the subconscious mind, encouraging it to accept his suggestions, whether or not they made logical sense.

"Those eyelids are so heavy they just don't want to work. And the harder you try, the harder they don't work. Like when you try to remember a word that's just on the tip of your tongue, the harder you try, the harder it runs away. And so now as you *try* to make them work, you notice that the harder you *try*, the harder it is to make them work...go ahead try...try...but the harder you try the more they stay glued together...Go ahead, try...."

As the doctor paused, I could see Chaim moving his eyelids but not quite pulling them open. After he struggled for a while the doctor began speaking again, but suddenly Chaim's eyes popped wide open. He sat up straight, staring at the doctor.

Dr. Aarons was taken aback, but quickly regained his composure and began speaking in his hypnotic voice, "Very good, Chaim...very good. You see you remain in control all the time. No one can take away your control from you...All you have to do is allow yourself to let go and to enjoy the feelings...so lean back and make yourself comfortable, as you resume your nice, deep, slow, relaxing breathing...You can close your eyes or leave them open as you wish...."

Chaim left his eyes open but resumed his slow breathing.

Dr. Aarons continued his "hypnotic patter" as he encouraged Chaim to relax more and more. Finally, once Chaim's eyes closed on their own, the doctor felt he was relaxed enough to continue with his deepening techniques.

"Now, Chaim, we will go on a journey together...a nice healing journey...My voice will go with you as you embark upon this journey...and my voice will accompany you all the time...At any time you can terminate the journey and come back to this room...as you wish....

"I'd like you to see yourself standing at the top of a flight of steps...ten steps leading down...At the bottom of the steps you will be in a beautiful and safe place. This is a place that is so beautiful to you...a place you love to be in...and it is a very safe place for you...no one can hurt you here...no one can do anything to you here...because this is your beautiful and safe place...and you can keep anyone out whom you do not wish to enter...It is your place and you have complete control over it....

"Now, spend a moment or two imagining where this beautiful and safe place is...It might be on the seaside, it might be in a green forest, it might be on the top of a mountain...it might be in your *beit medrash,* it might be even in an imaginary place like floating in a cloud...It can be anywhere at all, as long as you feel safe, in control, and happy in this place...as long as you know you are safe in this place and that no one can hurt you here...So spend a moment now finding your safe place in your mind and when you know where it is, just give me a little nod with your head...."

The doctor was silent and I could see that Chaim was thinking hard as his facial expression tensed up. Dr. Aarons noticed this as well.

"You don't have to think too hard about this," the doctor said. "Just remind yourself of a place where you really love to be and make it your beautiful and safe place. Just continue breathing and relaxing and your mind will bring the place to you...Maybe go back many years, maybe when you were a little boy...Where did you love to go and to be? It might even be to your grandmother's home...."

Dr. Aarons was silent. It took a very long time, but finally Chaim nodded his head slightly.

"Good! Very good! That's right. Now that you know where your safe and beautiful place is, we will go there together. As you stand at the head of the staircase I will count for you from ten to one and with each number that I count you will descend a step. With each step that you descend you will go even deeper into relaxation. When you come to the bottom of the stairs you will be in the depth of relaxation that is right for you...So are you ready to begin?"

Chaim nodded his head.

"Good...Feel your two feet firmly on the steps...Pay attention to what the steps are made of. Are they wood or stone or metal or marble? Perhaps they are covered with carpet, and if so, pay attention to the color of the carpet...There is a handrail on the wall next to you. Place your hand on the handrail and get ready to begin stepping down as I count...Beginning now..."

He counted very slowly. "Ten...nine....eight...seven...six...five... four...three...two...one...All the way down to the very bottom... Very, very good! Step into your beautiful and safe place and walk around...explore it...pay attention to what you find here...Use all of your senses to see, hear, feel, and experience your safe and beautiful place...perhaps even smell and taste your special place...Look around...Discover what there is to discover in this wonderful place...."

The doctor was silent, waiting for Chaim to explore his safe place.

After a moment, Chaim spoke up in a quiet voice, "I'm not there. I never went down the steps." He opened his eyes.

Dr. Aarons was rattled. He was not expecting this and neither was I. Once again, he hurriedly regained his composure and said in a matter-of-fact tone, "That's fine, Chaim. You don't have to go anywhere you don't want to go."

He rose from his chair and turned the lights up. He turned off the music. He then sat down again opposite Chaim.

"Was there any reason you didn't go down the steps, Chaim?"

"I don't know...Maybe when I stood there looking down I was afraid I might fall. So I just didn't go."

"I see...No problem. There are many ways to get to your safe place. We certainly don't have to go down steps. Would you like to go there in a different way?"

"I don't know...I'm not so sure my safe place really is safe."

"Why would that be?"

"Because no one knows from moment to moment what might happen. Surprises can happen even in the safest of places."

"I understand…The idea of creating a safe place is that you can imagine it any way you wish. You are the one who creates this place and no one else has access to it because it belongs entirely to you. So you can create it with built-in safety."

"I don't think the world works like that. I don't think we have total control over anything."

"OK. No problem. Next time you can ask Hashem to let His presence be felt in this place with you and protect it for you from anything unsafe."

"Why would Hashem agree to protect the place for me? How can I tell Hashem what to do?"

I could see that Dr. Aarons was feeling unnerved with the conversation. I was wondering how he would end the conversation in a way that would encourage Chaim to keep trying hypnosis.

"Look, Chaim, it's really very simple. You're not telling Hashem to do anything; you're asking Him to help you. We are meant to think positively. In the way that a person wants to go, from Heaven they will move him in that direction. Isn't that true?" Dr. Aarons was paraphrasing a phrase from Chazal.

"Yes, that is true. *B'derech she'adam rotzeh leileich bah molichin oso.*[13] But I really don't know if that applies to what we are doing."

"If we can create a safe place for you and from that place we'll be able to bring about healing, then surely in Heaven they would agree. Being healthier means you will be able to serve Hashem better, in a happier mood, and with more energy. Isn't that true?"

Chaim thought about that for a moment. "I guess it's true. But I will think about this some more. Maybe I'll speak to my rabbi about it."

"Sure. No problem. You must do what feels right to you. But if your rabbi would like to hear more about what I'm doing and trying to achieve, then he's welcome to call and talk to me about it."

The doctor rose from his chair, indicating that the session was over. Chaim rose as well. Dr. Aarons walked us out to the waiting room.

"Chaim, discuss whatever you need to with your rabbi and when you feel ready, I'll be very happy to serve you. You can book any future appointments with Dalya. Good day for now."

He shook Chaim's hand and we paid our bill. Silently, we walked toward the taxi stand. Chaim was thinking and I wanted to leave him undisturbed. I would find the opportune moment to discuss the session with him.

POST SESSION

On the ride home, Chaim actually wanted to talk about what had happened. He seemed to be struggling with something.

"You know," he said, "I can't understand why I didn't want to go down the steps. I really want Dr. Aarons to help me get over my attacks."

I was glad I'd been reading up on hypnosis. "I think you said it yourself, Chaim. Somewhere deep inside yourself you were afraid of going down the steps. Your logical mind doesn't have to understand why, or agree to that, but your subconscious mind has some reason for feeling unsafe. I believe that Dr. Aarons will find a way to gain the trust of your subconscious mind and then you will succeed beautifully."

"I don't know." Chaim sounded very unsure. "There's something about Dr. Aarons that I don't like. I wonder if it's his funny accent."

I was surprised with his comment and a bit annoyed that something so trivial might jeopardize the therapy. But I had to be objective and accepting of whatever Chaim was expressing. Who could know, maybe blaming the South African accent was merely an excuse for some other, more significant reason for holding back. I prayed that Hashem would give me the right words to put him at ease.

"That's interesting," I finally said, "I had the same feeling at first. But after a while I began liking his accent. I wonder if you'll get used to it and disregard it as you discover the value of the session."

Chaim didn't answer.

"If you were the therapist," I continued, "and your client told you he was afraid of going down the steps, and you wanted him to get to this safe place, how would you take him there?"

Chaim sat thinking. "Why do we need to go to the safe place at all?"

"Oh, it's really not important to call it a safe place. The idea is that you feel safe when you imagine yourself there. If you feel safe and protected, then you'll be willing to do what the doctor suggests to get over the attacks. If you don't feel safe you won't have the security to make changes or to follow his instructions. It's like if a child is crossing a very busy intersection on his own, with cars coming from all directions, he'd be petrified. But if he's holding his father's hand he wouldn't be frightened at all."

Chaim's face lit up with a smile. "I like your analogy. It really makes sense. OK, so how would I take my client to this safe place?" he asked himself. "I would take him on a ride in the car while wearing seat belts. I would drive very slowly and take time to enjoy the scenery. I would instruct him to tell me when we get to the 'place' and then we would get out of the car. We would walk through a gate that only the client had the key to, and this 'place' would be surrounded with a high wall so that no one could get in. There would be an alarm on the gate in case anyone tried to break in."

"Wow, that's amazing, Chaim. That's brilliant! I see that your subconscious mind knows exactly what you need!

"Chaim," I continued, "all you have to do next time is tell Dr. Aarons what you just told me. He keeps on saying that you should make yourself comfortable, that you should express yourself and say what feels good and what doesn't. So now you have your solution to what to do next."

"Not so fast." Chaim wanted to be the one in control. "I still want to speak to Rav Scheinerman and see what he has to say."

"Of course you do. If he thinks you should stop, you definitely will. And if he thinks you should continue, you now have an idea of how to do so. I'm sure Dr. Aarons will help you find the best way to continue."

Chaim didn't answer. He suddenly seemed very tired. The session must have taken a lot of energy out of him. He leaned back and closed his eyes. I couldn't tell if he fell asleep or not. But when we got home he went straight to bed and slept for a few hours.

The next day, he spent a long time speaking with Rav Scheinerman. Chaim told me that the *rav* was going to speak with Dr. Aarons and then call him back. The *rav* did call us that afternoon and it was decided that Chaim would go for another session. Afterward, he would again discuss his thoughts and feelings with Rav Scheinerman, who would then make a new assessment of the situation.

Chaim was happy with this plan, as he didn't want to feel pushed into going for hypnotherapy. I set up another appointment for the following week.

THE SECOND SESSION

Chaim had been instructed by Rav Scheinerman to speak up freely and let the doctor know if anything bothered him. He told him to disregard the South African accent and to make the effort to focus on the person behind the accent, the person who was there to help him.

The weather on the day of our second appointment was stormy, and we came into the office dripping. After Chaim got comfortable in the reclining chair, Dr. Aarons invited him to tell him what he thought about the last session. He also wished to hear if there was anything specific that he wanted or didn't want in the current session.

"Well, first of all, I don't want to go down the steps. It makes me feel very insecure. I would rather take a car and drive there myself. I will know when I get there and I'll let you know when that happens. Then, the safe place must be surrounded by a tall wall with a locked gate that only I have the key to. This way no one can enter without my permission. And lastly, I will only stay there as long as I feel comfortable, and not as long as you decide."

Chaim spoke forcibly and his words were followed by a crash of thunder for emphasis.

Dr. Aarons nodded his head approvingly. "Excellent, Chaim! You have clearly defined for yourself what makes you feel good and what doesn't. I'm really glad you were able to do that. Please feel free to continue to express your feelings as we go through the session.

"Chaim," he asked, "have you had any uncomfortable symptoms since the last time we met?"

"No."

"Have you felt any changes for the better during this time?"

"No. I feel about the same."

"I'm asking," said the doctor, "because you've discontinued taking your antianxiety medications and I was wondering if that had affected you in any way."

"I didn't notice any change," Chaim said simply.

"OK. Wonderful! So are you ready to start? Or is there anything else you would like to add?"

As Chaim opened his mouth to answer there was a very bright flash of lightening that caused the lights to flicker. The lightening was followed almost immediately by a tremendous clap of thunder. Chaim was visible startled and became rigid in the chair.

Dr. Aarons noticed his discomfort.

"Good thing we're having rain," he said as his way of trying to calm him. "We can always use more rain in this country!"

His words seemed to fall on deaf ears; Chaim remained in his rigid state. Dr. Aarons poured a glass of water and stretched out his hand to Chaim. Chaim didn't seem to notice the outstretched arm.

"Chaim," the doctor said firmly, "have a drink of water. You'll feel better."

Chaim looked at him as though awakening from a dream, and took the glass of water from Dr. Aarons. He gripped the glass tightly without drinking. I felt apprehensive seeing Chaim in this state; it was unnerving.

No one said anything for the next few minutes. We were waiting for Chaim to respond in some way. He did seem to be relaxing very slowly, when suddenly he became anxious again. There was an ambulance passing by outside and we could hear its siren loud and clear.

As the ambulance came closer and the wailing sound of the siren became stronger, Chaim suddenly jumped up from the chair. He threw the glass of water across the room. It shattered into a hundred pieces as it hit the wall, leaving an ugly blotch of wetness alongside the doctor's diplomas. He was shouting uncontrollably as he paced back and forth.

"What am I doing here? What are you trying to do to me?! Who brought me here to this horrid place?" He stared at me as he said that. His face had a frantic look on it.

Dr. Aarons rang a bell on his desk and the secretary walked in.

"Dalya, get the janitor here."

I could hear the agitation in his voice. Meanwhile, Chaim was still raving.

"You!" he pointed his finger at me. "You brought me here! Why? Why did you do it? Are you trying to kill me?!" He was screaming at me, at the walls, at the imaginary demons as he paced the room like a caged animal. "You hate me and want me to die! You're my worst enemy!"

I could feel my face turning beet red as the doctor and secretary stared at the scene in utter shock. I felt devastated; I wished I could sink down through the floor and disappear. Dalya hurried out as she'd been instructed by the doctor.

"Mrs. Perlman, please leave the room," the doctor commanded.

I knew Chaim wouldn't touch Dr. Aarons. If I left, I was afraid he would really believe that I was against him, and not out to help him. Although I was burning with shame and felt like running from the scene, I knew that doing so wouldn't help matters. I had to overcome my pride and do what I instinctively felt would be best for Chaim.

"It's OK, Dr. Aarons," I assured him. "He'll calm down in a minute or two."

I stepped closer to him and began talking in my very calming voice, as I had done on numerous past occasions. At first, he couldn't hear me as his ranting was drowning out my voice. But I carried on, using my most soothing tone and gentlest words. I believed he would be able to hear me in just a little bit, as the calming energy I was sending out was bound to quiet him down.

I saw in my peripheral vision Dr. Aarons leaving the room, and I knew he would be back in a few moments with the janitor. I had to get my husband under control before anyone tried to physically control him, probably none too gently. That would only add fuel to the fire.

"Chaim...Chaim...It's OK...It was just that loud noise that frightened you...You'll be all right...Hashem is here with you, Chaim...you're going to be fine...Just take it easy...Sit down now and breathe deeply...."

I saw his body start to relax as he slowed his breath down.

"That's right, Chaim!...You can do it...You're doing fine...."

I carried on with my calming words, and finally he did sit down and began breathing deeply as I directed him. By the time Dr. Aarons returned with the janitor, he was sitting docilely in the armchair, appearing very innocent. His head was slightly bent and he was looking at the floor.

Dr. Aarons was amazed at the transformation. "I can't believe that you got him to calm down. What did you do?" he asked me.

"He's used to my talking to him during an attack. He's become accustomed to my voice and the words I use to calm him. Unfortunately, I've had more than enough experience dealing with this when he has his attacks. He won't be responsive to you now. He gets so exhausted after an episode and usually goes to sleep for several hours afterward. I don't even think he would hear you talking to him if you tried."

Dr. Aarons asked the janitor to sweep up the glass from the floor. He then sat down at his desk and jotted down some notes in Chaim's file. He finished and looked at me with a questioning glance.

"Was this a typical 'attack'? Is this an example of why you came for treatment?" he asked.

"This was slightly more violent than previous ones. I think he was frightened twice, both by the thunder and the ambulance. But it is very similar in style to his other attacks. I think he directed all of his venom at me because there was no one else to blame. At home, he divides the shouting and the blaming between me and the children."

"Why didn't he blame me?" the doctor wanted to know.

"I can't say for sure, but maybe because you aren't yet a part of his memory relating to his attacks. Whatever is bothering him, you don't exist for him when he's in that state.

"That's just my guess...You would probably know better than me why he acted the way he did." I too was beginning to feel exhausted and didn't have the energy to talk anymore. I just wanted to get home already.

"That makes sense, Mrs. Perlman, and most likely that is the explanation. Do you want to set up another appointment?" Dr. Aarons was jotting down some more notes.

I was surprised at the question. I couldn't imagine that Chaim would agree to come back.

"I don't know," I answered. "He might not want to continue treatment. I'll have to speak to him about it when he gets back to normal."

"I understand," Dr. Aarons said. "I don't want him to leave therapy with a bad feeling. I think we both agree that it was the ambulance siren that caused his attack, not the therapy itself."

"Of course, you're not to blame in the slightest. It was just a freak occurrence that triggered things. But I have no way of knowing what he'll be thinking or feeling about what happened here today. I'll have to be in touch with you after I talk to him."

Dr. Aarons nodded his head and closed the file. He suggested that I put Chaim back on the antianxiety medication, at least temporarily.

We both got up and I led Chaim to the waiting room. I took out my checkbook to pay for the visit.

"There will be no charge for today, Mrs. Perlman," the doctor said.

"Oh! That's very kind of you." I really appreciated his consideration. "Dalya, would you please order a taxi for us."

While we waited for the taxi to come, I put a call through to Alexander. I would need his help getting Chaim up the three flights of stairs and into bed. He assured me that he would be at our home in half an hour. Within a few minutes we were on our way home.

On the ride home, Chaim fell asleep. This was his usual response to attacks. I knew I would have to speak to him about his outburst eventually, but I certainly was in no mood to do it right then. Although I had put on a nice front for the doctor and Dalya, I was still literally shaking with humiliation — and fear for the future.

The real Chaim was kind, generous, considerate, and gentle. This was a perverted likeness of Chaim that somehow took complete control of him. Intellectually, I knew that, but I had been wounded to the core. Old wounds had opened up. My emotional turmoil caused me to feel anger, even though I knew it was unjustified. I realized I would have to work on my *middos* and learn to let go of the anger. I needed to transcend the feelings of resentment, bitterness, and shame, so that I could forgive in a real and meaningful way.

This was a challenge that I had to deal with. I had started the process numerous times in the past, and it would probably take years before I completely got beyond it. But I was determined to succeed.

THE THIRD SESSION

Rav Scheinerman felt Chaim should have a third session with Dr. Aarons. After all, no therapy had been done at the second session. He also didn't want Chaim to remain with the impression that hypnotherapy or Dr. Aarons had caused his attack. He had to be clear that it was the ambulance siren that caused it and that the hypnosis had nothing to do with it. The *rav* felt that it was important for Chaim to remain open to hypnosis.

After Rav Scheinerman spoke to Chaim at length he agreed to another session. The *rav* pointed out that if after three more sessions Chaim felt that nothing positive was happening, we could then conclude that Dr. Aarons was not the appropriate *shaliach* for us. In that case, we could still find a different hypnotherapist who might have more success in treating Chaim.

Once again, we found ourselves in Dr. Aarons' office. I felt awkward when Dalya greeted me, wondering what was going through her mind as she surely revisited our last "session." Chaim was introverted and seemed unaffected by his surroundings. I prayed that Dr. Aarons would have a way to get through to Chaim's subconscious mind and succeed in helping him.

"Come in, come in!" Dr. Aarons was being his most friendly, relaxing self as he welcomed us into his office. "Make yourselves comfortable. Good to see you again!"

The doctor shook Chaim's hand while Chaim mumbled a greeting. He didn't seem very enthusiastic at being back in this place. It would be a tribute to Dr. Aarons' expertise if he could get his recalcitrant patient to open up.

Dr. Aarons led Chaim over to the recliner and they both seated themselves. From my position, I could see my husband's face and Dr. Aarons' back.

"So, how have you been feeling these days?" Dr. Aarons' voice expressed real interest.

"OK," Chaim answered quietly.

"Are you taking the antianxiety pills again?"

"Yes."

"Have there been any special noises that caused an attack?"

"No."

"Would you like to tell me something about how these past few days have been for you? Or maybe you can tell me what you've been thinking or feeling or about any concerns you may have."

"No."

Oh, no! Chaim, can't you be more cooperative? I screamed mentally. Chaim did not get my telepathic message and sat there without saying a word.

Dr. Aarons decided to make the best of it.

"Wonderful, my friend! I'm so glad that things have quieted down for you! Let's get right on with it."

He remembered the technique Chaim had described to him the previous time for bringing him to his safe place.

"Can you tell me, Chaim, which car you will use to get to your safe place?"

Chaim's eyes turned upward in thought before he responded, and this was a good sign. The doctor was nudging Chaim to go inward to "see" something internally. This was a first step in hypnosis, the journey into his private inner world.

Dr. Aarons then asked Chaim to tell him what speed would feel comfortable while he was driving his vehicle. Slowly but surely, he drew Chaim into visualizing the journey to his safe place. I breathed a sigh of relief when I realized that he was actually there.

Dr. Aarons took his time going deeper and deeper, checking to see if Chaim was with him as they progressed. I understood that he wanted to discover what Chaim was experiencing when he heard the sounds that triggered his attacks. I could sense that Chaim felt "safe" in his safe place.

"And now, Chaim, that you have explored your safe and beautiful pace...you can relax in a comfortable beach chair or even lie on the soft grass...or relax in whichever way feels best to you...and spend a few moments enjoying the pleasure of being here...That's right...breathing deeply and slowly...as you breathe in the calm tranquility of this wonderful place...."

Dr. Aarons' voice was very soothing and sleep-inducing. I felt like closing my eyes listening to him, but forced them to stay open as I did not want to miss a moment of whatever would transpire.

He was silent for several moments to allow Chaim to feel the tranquility that he had been talking about.

"Chaim," he continued, "I'd like you to get up now and walk over to the wall surrounding your safe place...There is a one-way window that allows you to look out, although no one can look in. I want you to look out now…" He waited for a moment or two. "Outside your safe place there is a man standing there. Can you see him?" Chaim nodded his head slightly. "He has some kind of problem. I'm not sure what it is. Can you see what is wrong with him?"

It took Chaim a long time to answer. Finally, he started speaking very softly.

"His head is smashed and is bandaged up…There is blood on the bandages."

"Can you see his face?" the doctor asked. "Can you tell me what expression his face has? Is he happy, sad, angry, or maybe frightened?…What is this man feeling?"

Again, it took a while until Chaim answered. "He's scared…"

"Do you know why?…Or would you like to ask him why he's scared?"

Chaim was silent for a very long time. The doctor then asked very gently, "Can you ask him why he is scared? Maybe we can help him…."

Chaim did not take the bait; he remained silent.

"What does he say, Chaim?…Can you hear him?"

Chaim remained silent.

After a lengthy pause, the doctor continued, "Chaim, tell him he doesn't have to tell you why he is scared…He can keep his secret…It's OK…We don't need to know. He will tell us whenever he feels ready….

"Would you like to bring him into the safe place…so that he can feel safe and doesn't need to be scared anymore?"

Chaim looked like he was debating the issue in his mind. Finally, he answered so quietly that I could barely hear him. "Yes, he can come in…but he must be checked first…."

"Will you check him, Chaim?" the doctor asked.

Chaim nodded his head.

"What are you going to check him for?"

Once again, his voice was so quiet that I had to strain to hear. "That he has no stones in his pockets…Or sirens…."

"Very good, Chaim! You will check him very soon...for whatever you wish to check for...But first, call to him now...and invite him in...You can meet him at the gate...where you will check him...Let me know when he is there."

The doctor waited patiently for Chaim to let him know when the man got to the gate. After a few minutes, Chaim spoke up. "He doesn't want to come."

Dr. Aarons must have felt frustrated but he hid it superbly in his response. "Chaim tell him that he doesn't have to come now...if he doesn't want to. He can come in tomorrow...or the next day...or whenever he feels like it. Just let him know...that he will feel very good in the safe place...and he will heal easily and quickly...in this magical place...He will heal easily and quickly...when he comes in...He has nothing to fear...only to know that he will...heal easily and quickly here...Does he understand?"

From my reading of the hypnosis texts I understood that Dr. Aarons was speaking to the two parts of Chaim, the part that wanted to do the therapy and heal and the part that was afraid for whatever reason. He repeated the words "he will heal easily and quickly" several times, because repetition would make the hypnosis more effective and powerful.

"The man understands."

"Chaim, tell the man that you only want to help him...Is that true, Chaim?"

He nodded his head.

"Good!" Dr. Aarons said the word very emphatically. "Does he believe you...that you only want to help him?"

After a long pause, Chaim nodded his head. "Excellent!...Now tell him goodbye...and also that you will be waiting at the gate to let him in whenever he wants to come...Is that true, Chaim?"

This time Chaim's nod came rather quickly. I could imagine Dr. Aarons' sigh of relief. This was the right time to conclude the session.

"Did he say anything to you...as you told him goodbye?"

Chaim's pause was brief before answering. "He said he wants to see me next week."

This time I could imagine a big smile settling on Dr. Aarons' face. "Wonderful!...Are you ready to meet him next week, Chaim?"

Chaim nodded his head.

"Good...Tell him how much you are looking forward to meeting him next week...And that you wish him to feel well until you meet again...and then he will feel even better...."

"Now, watch him walk off...until you can no longer see him...Good!...OK, you can open the gate and get into your car and drive back to this room...."

Dr. Aarons gave him the cues, slowly bringing him to greater and greater awareness and alertness. After several minutes, Chaim was all the way back and he opened his eyes. He looked quite relaxed.

"Well, hello!" Dr. Aarons must have been smiling at Chaim. "How are you feeling?"

"Good," Chaim said simply.

"Do you have any comments or questions about your session?"

"I really felt like I was driving that car." Chaim looked surprised.

"Good! That shows what an excellent hypnosis subject you are. I must say, you did very well. How long do you think you were in hypnosis?"

"Uh, maybe...fifteen minutes."

"Take a look at your watch, Chaim. It was more like forty minutes."

"What!" Chaim was shocked as he took note of the time. "It didn't feel that long at all! How could that be?"

"That's another indication that you had a good session. One of the classic signs of hypnotic trance is when time becomes distorted. It's like when you dream, and a short period of time seems long or a long period of time seems short. Do you have any other questions?"

Chaim thought for a moment and said that he didn't. Dr. Aarons gave Chaim a drink of water. After he finished drinking, the doctor stood up and walked us to the door. "Make your next appointment with Dalya and I'll see you next week."

POST SESSION

On the way home, I asked Chaim what he thought about the session.

"I don't know," he answered. "It was weird seeing that man there with the bloody bandages. I don't know if I like him!"

I was shocked at his answer. Apparently, he didn't realize that he was talking about a part of himself. Or maybe he did. I guess we all have parts of ourselves that we dislike, the part that eats too much cake when we're trying to lose weight, the part that gets angry and "loses it" when we've made a resolution to react to situations with "calm," or the part that stays in bed when we've decided to accomplish a lot that day.

Now that I thought about it, I remembered how I had "hated" my dyslexic self when I failed my spelling tests, or when I couldn't read fluently in class, or when people took unfair advantage of me and I was too shy to speak up.

How could I "hate" that poor child? Was she at fault for having the disabilities she was born with or the ones she acquired as she went through life? How many times do we blame ourselves, yell at ourselves, and get so angry at ourselves for our shortcomings. Sometimes we even inflict self-punishment! Perhaps a better way would be to genuinely try to understand and have compassion toward that part of ourselves in order to help it. Perhaps what we need to do is to invite the "hurt self" into a safe place and help him overcome his fears by listening to him, trying to understand him, and by offering help that could strengthen him.

Suddenly, a whole new way of dealing with problems opened up before me. I really liked this hypnosis technique, of seeing different aspects of the self as separate entities. The question remained, would it work for Chaim?

"Chaim," I said in a very soft and curious-sounding voice. "What is it about 'the man' that you don't like?"

"It's hard to put my finger on it, but I think it's that he's undisciplined and does nasty things to people. That's the feeling I get about him. I think maybe he takes advantage of his situation and makes excuses for himself because he is injured. He acts more hurt than he really is."

"How do you know all that, Chaim? Did you speak to him? Do you know him from somewhere else?"

"No, I never met him before. It's just a gut feeling I have, like an instinct."

"Maybe you could help him," I said. "It certainly sounds like he needs help. You do such a great job helping the boys in yeshiva, I'm sure you could help him too. He wants to meet you next week, so I guess that means that he wants your help."

"You know, we're not talking about a real person!" He suddenly spoke loudly and seemed agitated. "He's only a figment of my imagination. Who's there to help? It's better to forget the whole thing!"

I wasn't sure how to respond. I certainly did not want to spoil the work Dr. Aarons had done. I prayed to Hashem to give me the right words. I started off hesitantly, waiting to see Chaim's reaction.

"Chaim, let's not jump to conclusions. I'm sure Dr. Aarons knows how doing this can help. If you want, we can call him up when we get home and ask. Do you want to call him?"

"I don't know." He was beginning to shut down.

"Maybe Rav Scheinerman will understand how it can help. It's always a good idea to talk to him when things don't seem clear."

Chaim remained silent. I was not going to end the conversation with a wall of silence. I wanted Chaim to feel as positive as I did. So in my cheeriest voice possible I said, "Boy, I wish I was in that recliner and had the opportunity to help that poor man. Let's ask Rav Scheinerman if I can switch places with you next week. OK?"

My words were meant as a joke and I was hoping that Chaim would laugh. But he didn't catch the joke and it fell flat.

Instead he very deliberately said, "Sure! I'll be happy if you take my place next week!"

I made one last effort to rectify the situation. "If Rav Scheinerman says no to our switching places, is it OK for me to make my own appointment with Dr. Aarons?"

"Why would you want to do that?" Chaim was puzzled.

"I think I may have a 'wounded woman' inside of me that needs some help."

I suddenly saw a shift in his expression, as though the sun was emerging from behind the clouds. I think he finally caught on to who "the man" was and why he needed help. Everything that had happened in the session now made sense. He sat quietly, introspective, pondering the implications. He remained that way till the end of our trip.

At home, he ate something and went to bed. He slept for several hours. I used this time to call Rav Scheinerman and tell him about the session. He too was happy with what had taken place. He felt the doctor was getting closer to the crux of the problem.

"I'm hopeful that his methods will bring about positive results. I'll speak to Chaim in the evening and encourage him to book another session," the *rav* said as we concluded our discussion.

THE FOURTH SESSION

I was looking forward to this session; intuitively I felt that something conclusive would happen this time. Chaim did not share his feelings with me about coming to the appointment, although I had asked him on several occasions for his input.

Dr. Aarons was his usual friendly, upbeat self.

"Hello there, my friend!" Dr. Aarons extended his hand to Chaim in greeting. "How are you today?"

"*Baruch Hashem*, fine," Chaim replied in a subdued tone while shaking the doctor's hand.

I wondered why he was so passive when interacting with Dr. Aarons. It was quite clear that the doctor wanted to help him.

I was so positive about the sessions that I felt that some words of gratitude needed to be expressed. So, although my shyness made it difficult, I decided to speak up. I felt that not doing so would appear ungrateful. And this I could not tolerate in myself.

"Dr. Aarons," I said with enthusiasm, "I'm really excited to be here today. And I'm sure Chaim is as well. I really feel we are moving in the right direction. I'm very impressed with your expertise!"

I took a deep breath after my great effort. But I was happy that I managed to get the words out. I could see Dr. Aarons appreciated them, even though Chaim did not add any comments of his own.

"Thank you, Mrs. Perlman. With G-d's help we will get to the bottom of Chaim's difficulty and watch it disappear." He didn't seem bothered by Chaim's lack of agreement.

He then led Chaim over to the recliner and they both seated themselves.

"Chaim, you're looking well today! What can you tell me about these last few days? Have you noticed anything different than usual?"

Chaim pondered the question. "I can't think of anything," he finally answered.

"No attacks? No bouts of anxiety?"

"No. Things are relatively quiet."

"Good! Very good my friend. You're really doing well!" Chaim smiled slightly in return.

I sensed that the doctor wished, with his small talk, to encourage Chaim to relax and open up.

"Are you ready to begin your journey?"

Chaim nodded his head, adjusted his position in the chair and leaned back.

Dr. Aarons began the induction in a similar fashion to the previous session. Chaim went down relatively quickly this time. He was reliving a familiar process and his brain complied more easily with the suggestions.

I was very interested in the process of how one induces a hypnotic state and listened closely to Dr. Aarons' "hypnotic patter."

"Now that you are again in your beautiful and safe place... take a moment to explore it...and notice if it's the same...or if it has changed in any way...That's it...take your time to feel the pleasure...

the beauty...the peacefulness...the tranquility this place is giving you...Notice whatever there is to notice...."

He was quiet for a bit as Chaim, so to speak, explored his safe and beautiful place. After an appropriate pause, Dr. Aarons asked, "Is your safe and beautiful place just as safe and beautiful as it was before?"

"Yes, it is."

"Is the wall surrounding it still there? Is anything different?"

"The wall is there, but the gate is open," Chaim answered.

"Is it alright to leave the gate open...? Do you want to close it?"

"I want to close it. I don't want just anyone walking in."

"Do you have any idea who opened the gate? Was it closed last time when you left?"

Chaim was quiet for several moments. Finally, he spoke softly, "I think I left it open when I left last time."

"Maybe there is no need to close the gate," Dr. Aarons suggested. "Maybe there is no one who will walk in."

"That man is here somewhere. I know he is here somewhere." Chaim spoke slowly, with effort. I wondered if that meant he was in a deep trance.

Dr. Aarons suddenly became more authoritative. "Will you please ask him to come now? Let him know that we are waiting for him."

Chaim was silent for several minutes. Then he said, "I called him but he didn't come. He is hiding."

"Tell him we have some good things for him...some good news...Let him know we want to help him."

Dr. Aarons waited for a response but Chaim was silent. He then spoke very firmly, "Chaim, do you want to help him?"

Chaim took a long time in answering. "I don't know. I'm not sure if I like that man."

I couldn't see his face but sensed that Dr. Aarons was surprised. I think he thought that this session would move along very smoothly, but unfortunately Chaim's resistance was very tangible.

"What might there be that you don't like about him, Chaim?"

"He's ugly. He's offensive."

"Is that his fault? Wasn't he hurt in some way by someone or something that he could not control?"

"I don't know."

"Would you like to ask him how he was hurt? Would you like to know what happened to him? What could have made him like this?"

Chaim seemed to be debating with himself. I couldn't understand why he was being so oppositional. Didn't he want to be healed? What was he afraid of? He didn't answer the question and his silence was becoming oppressive.

Finally, Dr. Aarons said, "You know what…Let's not ask him what happened. Let's just try to help him in other ways…Maybe he is hungry. Let's put out some tasty food for him and then maybe he will come…Would you like to do that?"

Chaim answered reluctantly, "OK."

Dr. Aarons instructed Chaim to prepare a plate of tempting food, leave it outside the gate, and then to let him know when the man appeared.

We sat in silence for quite a while. After several minutes, Dr. Aarons spoke. "Can you see him, Chaim? Has he come for the food?"

"No," was Chaim's curt reply.

"Chaim, do I have your permission to talk to 'the man'? Maybe he'll answer me." Dr. Aarons was trying whatever strategy he could think of. I hoped this one would work.

Chaim was slow to answer but finally agreed.

"Hello there!" Dr. Aarons used a soft and friendly tone. "We have been waiting for you for quite a while now…Do you remember telling us last time that you wanted to visit with us this week…? We brought you some delicious food…It's waiting for you here by the gate…Please come toward us….It's quite safe here…We want to help you…We're your friends and we're here to help."

Dr. Aarons changed his tone as he addressed Chaim. "Can you see him, Chaim? Is he there?"

"I see him. He is coming slowly to the gate."

I let out a sigh of relief. I was sitting on the edge of my chair, wondering what would happen next.

"What does he look like, Chaim?....Can you see the expression on his face?...Has he changed in any way?" I assumed that Dr. Aarons needed to know if there was any change, for the better or the worse.

"He looks worried. His bandages are very bloody...more than last time."

"Is it alright if I speak to him again, Chaim?"

"If you want to," was his morose reply. There was not a shred of enthusiasm on Chaim's part. I felt like crying.

"Good..." Once again, the doctor changed his tone of voice. "Hello there. I am Dr. Aarons. I'm a friend...And Chaim, he's also a friend...Help yourself to the food...Take as much as you want...When you finish eating, please tell me your name."

After an appropriate pause, Dr. Aarons addressed Chaim with his altered tone of voice. "Has he finished eating...? Were you able to hear him say his name?"

Chaim's answer came more readily this time. "He ate a little and then he vomited. He's turning to go away."

"Is it alright if I speak to him again?" The doctor barely waited for Chaim's answer, as he hurriedly continued. "Hello there! Would you like a drink of water? Please don't go...We want to help you...Have a drink of water first..." He changed his tone and then spoke to Chaim. "Chaim please give him a glass of water...."

Chaim simply said, "He's gone."

Dr. Aarons seemed to deflate like a punctured balloon. I myself was disappointed beyond words. The session, in essence, was over. How would the doctor draw it to a close now?

"All right. I'm glad he appeared and ate a little. Maybe next time he will trust us enough to take some more from us and perhaps to enter the safe place. Would you like that Chaim?"

"I don't know. I don't think he'll come."

Dr. Aarons brought Chaim out of hypnosis slowly and he opened his eyes.

The doctor had recovered enough to reassume his smile and cheery voice.

"You know, Chaim, the fact that 'the man' vomited and walked off is no indication of failure. It merely points out to us that he is excessively sensitive. We'll have to learn to tune in to his wavelength." Chaim sat mute. His silence was ominous.

"So, Chaim, how do you feel?" Dr. Aarons asked very nonchalantly.

"Tired."

"Yes, I can imagine that seeing 'the man' with bloody bandages and vomiting would make you feel exhausted. Why do you think he wouldn't stay or come in?"

"He doesn't trust us."

"Would you be willing to make the effort to gain his trust?"

"No, it's too tiring!" Chaim seemed slightly angry, as though being given a job he didn't want.

"That's quite alright, Chaim. Do you have any questions about what happened today?"

"No." Chaim seemed not to care or take any interest in what had happened.

I was full of questions and could not restrain myself. "I have some questions," I said to Dr. Aarons. "Is this the right time to ask them?"

"I think that since your husband is tired we shouldn't delay his return home. I'll be happy to answer your questions by phone. You can call me at this number tonight after nine p.m." He underlined a number on his business card and handed it to me.

I put the card in my bag. We all stood up and he led us out of the room. He shook Chaim's hand warmly and wished him the very best, although he failed to say that we should schedule the next appointment with Dalya. My heart was heavy, filled to bursting with the shards of my shattered hopes.

After we arrived home, as usual Chaim ate something and went to sleep for several hours. While he slept I called Rav Scheinerman.

"It's Mrs. Perlman," I said when the *rav* came on the line. "I wanted to tell the *rav* how the last hypnosis session went."

"Yes, please do."

"It was awful! I'm so upset and disappointed! Chaim was completely uncooperative with the doctor's efforts at helping him. Instead of him having a productive session with the wounded man, Chaim just let him walk away. The doctor tried in so many ways, but couldn't get into conversation with the man. Chaim was totally apathetic and uncaring about what was happening. The doctor didn't even tell us to make another appointment before we left. I think he gave up hope of getting anywhere with Chaim."

My monologue burst forth emotionally and I felt spent. But it was good to express my frustration and distress. Just knowing that I did not have to endure my burden alone was calming.

"I'll speak to Dr. Aarons. I'll find out if there's any point in Chaim's continuing treatment with him."

"He told me to call after nine p.m. if I had questions." I gave the *rav* the number the doctor had underlined on his business card.

When I called the doctor later that night, he shared his assessment of the situation.

"I practice what's called a direct or an authoritarian style of hypnosis, which doesn't work well with resistant patients. What might work for Chaim is Ericksonian or Indirect Hypnosis."

"What's that?" I asked simply.

"This technique was developed by an American psychiatrist called Milton Erickson. He's in his late seventies and still teaching his method of hypnosis. It works very well in cases exhibiting resistance. The style is so 'indirect' that the patient is not even aware that he is being hypnotized. He's never told directly to do anything. All the suggestions are given in a very subtle and indirect way, through stories and metaphors, which bypass the conscious mind and go directly into the subconscious mind. Dr. Erickson has achieved tremendous success with his method and has become something of a legend in his lifetime.

"Unfortunately," Dr. Aarons continued, "I don't know of any hypnotist in Israel who practices indirect hypnosis. I suggest you contact the Society of Ericksonian Hypnotism in the USA to find out if they know of practitioners in this country or in Europe. Other than that, I can only suggest that you turn to different methods of treatment, such as psychotherapy or Gestalt therapy. I'm not sure if you could find a Gestalt practitioner here either but you could try advertising for one."

I felt broken by his words. We seemed to be up against a brick wall. I knew that Dr. Aarons had done his best to help. He had persevered in the face of resistance from the beginning. I could only feel gratitude for his brave efforts.

"Dr. Aarons," I said, "I thank you from the bottom of my heart. I know you did your utmost to help Chaim. Perhaps one day we'll find a solution, and I'll be happy to let you know the happy ending to our story."

"Well, thank you for your kind words, Mrs. Perlman. I certainly will be thrilled to hear that happy ending. Much luck to you and your husband. If you ever want to consult with me I will be happy to be of service."

So ended our conversation. And so ended our first effort at finding a solution for Chaim's ailment. We were back at square one. Where would we find the right *shaliach* to move us forward in our quest for healing?

CHAPTER SEVEN

In Continued Quest of Healing

INVESTIGATING OPTIONS

Now it was up to me to discover someone who might be able to help my poor husband. I turned to the yellow pages of the phone books of all the cities in Israel. I called every hypnotist I could find with my inquiries about Ericksonian Hypnosis. Again and again, I was disappointed in my search. However, as a result of my efforts, I had compiled a list of highly successful hypnotists in indirect hypnosis abroad. Once again, I consulted with Dr. Aarons.

"Dr. Aarons, are you familiar with any of these hypnotists that I found out about?" I asked. I read off the names I had on my list.

"I'm not familiar with most of them, but I can tell you that I have great respect for Dr. Roy Trapper[14] in Redondo Beach, California and for Stephen Rivers[15] in London. Stephen was the first practitioner of Ericksonian Hypnosis in Great Britain and has actually trained hundreds of students in the school he founded for indirect hypnosis.

"I have personally attended workshops of both of these hypnotists and although each has his unique style, I'm very impressed with their methodology. Trapper spends a lot of time with Parts Therapy and also Past Life Regression. You might need more sessions with him than perhaps with another practitioner. On the other hand, Rivers has developed a very efficient and speedy way of working indirectly with patients. He has numerous cases of one-session 'miracle' cures attributed to him. I believe he would be successful in working with Chaim."

"Thank you so much, doctor, for your time and input. It's very helpful."

I put down the receiver. Would we have to move to *chutz la'aretz* in order for Chaim to get well? Could we, and of course Chaim himself, endure the suffering until we found a cure? What would happen to our marriage and our children?

I rested my throbbing head on my arms and closed my eyes. I knew I couldn't figure out on my own the best route to take. I needed the advice of *daas Torah* and determined to call Rav Scheinerman that evening.

I spoke to the *rav* late that night. He was very empathetic.

"I know it is hard contemplating leaving Eretz Yisrael," his voice was kind, "but if no treatment of value turns up here within the year and Chaim's attacks don't resolve or at least improve on their own, then going to London might be an option. You would have the advantage of living within a religious Jewish community, whereas if you were to live somewhere in California, you most likely would be lacking one.

"Continue to enquire about Stephen Rivers' method of cure. Try to get an idea of the length of time treatment might take. And this is very important: Do your utmost to speak personally to people who have undergone these supposedly 'one-session' cures and find out whether they remained symptom-free in the long run."

My work was cut out for me. While trying various types of more conventional therapies in Israel during the next few months, simultaneously I invested a good part of my free time in tracking down people who had given testimonials in the written materials I had received from Stephen Rivers' British School of Ericksonian Hypnosis. I actually managed to speak to five of them and was amazed to learn of the degree of healing these people had undergone. For some, the process had been instantaneous, and for others, it had been more of a gradual evolution. I even had an in-depth conversation with Stephen Rivers himself. I was stunned to hear that although he never attained the title of doctor or professor, by honing his skills as a master hypnotherapist over the years, he had been successful in transforming the lives of hundreds of clients. He had no doubts that he could resolve Chaim's problem within a relatively short amount of time. But, he said, one could never know before meeting the patient what exactly was involved. He provided me with a list of names and numbers of his students who had full-time hypnosis practices in Great Britain and suggested I contact them. They would be able to tell me more about the successes they had encountered in their work, particularly with trauma.

I did exactly that and worried over our ballooning phone bill. I prayed that the time, effort, and money that I was expending would eventually bear fruit. I accumulated a thick file of notes and made a summary of all relevant information to present to Rav Scheinerman. After studying the material carefully, the *rav* called me up.

"You have spent months and months trying everything you can here in Eretz Yisrael. Nothing has worked. It sounds like the best option is London," Rav Scheinerman said. "Chaim's brother moved to London last year. Is he still there?"

"Yes," I said. "His wife, Yaffa, is English and she really missed home. Ari is teaching in a yeshiva in Stamford Hill."

"Wonderful! So you have someone in London with connections to help you, if you do make the move. I also know *rabbanim* in several of the *yeshivos* there. I'm sure things could be arranged for Chaim to be employed in one of them. The London religious *kehillah* is always in need of qualified *melamdim*. Besides, there are various tzedakah organizations that can help with medical expenses if need be. So really, there's no reason to worry. Please think about it."

I got Chaim to sit down with me and write a letter to Ari and Yaffa explaining our predicament and tentative plans for moving to London. I wanted him to be involved in the planning and decision making going on in our lives. My desire was for him to become a more active participant rather than a passive one in his healing process. He actually penned most of the questions he had about living in London and formulated many of the requests to his brother and sister-in-law about exploring job possibilities and school options for the children. I was very encouraged by his involvement.

Over the following weeks, Rav Scheinerman had frequent conversations with Chaim about the move. As he got used to the idea, Chaim was becoming increasingly comfortable with it. Luckily for both of us, Chaim was not intimidated by change; he rather looked at it as adding to the spice of life. His knowledge of several languages, his natural self-confidence, as well as his innovative ways, made him a person who was open to trying new endeavors.

One day, a thick envelope arrived in the mail. Shoshi was thrilled to get a load of stamps from Great Britain for her collection. Ari and Yaffa had written us an encouraging letter about life in the London *chareidi* community. And the London children sent drawings to their Israeli cousins of double-decker buses and bridges and towers.

And so, with the passage of time, I was happy to see that Chaim was beginning to look forward to our move to England in his quest for healing.

CHAPTER EIGHT

The Move to England

THE LAST SUKKOS

The Yom Kippur fast had just ended. It was hard to believe that a year had passed already since the momentous Yom Kippur War. Life in Israel was more or less back to normal. I couldn't say the same for us. We were now standing at the commencement of a new chapter in our lives and to me that felt as though we were standing at the edge of a precipice. How would it play out? I wondered.

I was grateful to see that Chaim was feeling good after the fast. He even wanted to begin working on our sukkah and called Joe, Mike's former study partner, to join him.

Joe graciously used every opportunity to come over and help Chaim whenever he could. That night he came with two friends from yeshiva and they put up the sukkah walls in record time. I made sure to have chocolate cake on hand, as it was still a trigger for good feelings between us. Whenever the chocolate cake appeared Joe would quip, "Nothing beats homemade chocolate cake, Mrs. Perlman!" and we would both burst out laughing.

He had come a long way since that initial lesson with Chaim after which he had first tasted my chocolate cake. He was a fine young bachelor who now called himself Yosef, although we still called him Joe. I was always scanning the young women I knew for someone suitable for him.

Now that we were on the verge of leaving Eretz Yisrael I wondered what would happen with Joe. Maybe I could find someone for him in England. I needed to dredge up every possible reason for me to make this move, because whenever I thought of it my stomach tied in knots. I knew we needed to go, I wanted to go, but I was still sad at leaving my true home, my friends, my work, and my myriad connections. If I could possibly find a *shidduch* for Joe over there, that would encourage me to feel more positive about the move.

Joe, too, was sad with our soon-to-be departure. He shared a close bond with Chaim, who loved him as a younger brother. He promised us that if he ever felt the need to stretch his wings and take flight, he would visit us in our new home. Chaim repeatedly assured him that there would always be an available bed for him in the Perlman home, no matter where we ended up.

There was so much to do and I had to focus on how to get through Sukkos. But that didn't mean that I hadn't done my packing and preparing the house for our renters who would move in the day after we left. The physical work was hard for me as, once more, I was a lady-in-waiting. But who said that hard was bad and easy was good? "*L'fum tzarah agra* — the reward is in proportion to the exertion."[16]

I had to train myself to think of every challenge as a step leading me to some coveted goal. The goal of moving to England was, first and foremost, to attain healing for Chaim. What could be more valuable than that?

I wanted the children to be left with good memories of this Sukkos, so I sat with them and we made loads of beautiful decorations together. We then hung them and the old decorations while singing *yom tov* songs. I took lots of photos of the children as they cut, colored, and pasted, and then as they pushed thumbtacks into the walls and cleaned and swept. I wanted a record of every bit of meaningful moment experienced before we actually left Eretz Yisrael. Who knew when we'd be back again?

We had a memorable *chag* with lots of good food, visitors, and outings. It was public knowledge that we were moving soon and everyone, from great-aunt Dina to the milkman, took the opportunity to visit us on Chol Hamoed.

One evening, Rabbi Reichman came over with his yeshiva boys and their musical instruments and we had a mini *Simchas Beis HaSho'eivah* in our sukkah. Bina came, too, with her children, laden with delicious cakes and *kugels*.

The music and singing were awesome; a memory I would not easily forget. For the grand finale, all the men joined hands in a dance around our sukkah table. Chaim's face was shining like I hadn't seen in a long time. Someone videoed the whole thing and gave us a copy before we left. It was the best present anyone could have given us.

Sukkos was over all too soon. Our flight was scheduled for ten days later. The children had their goodbye parties in *gan* and school. My friends, not to be outdone, surprised me one evening with a farewell party in Merry Sherman's house. Bina gave a moving speech, which made me cry, and the ladies presented me with a goodbye gift, a lovely wall clock with a scene of ancient Yerushalayim in the background. Someone had written an inspiring poem about cycles of time and how before long, I would once more be back in the Holy Land. But for the meantime, the clock would grace my London home and remind me of how fast time flies by until, once more, I would be back in my real home.

LONDON CONNECTIONS

Rav Scheinerman, true to his word, had contacted his acquaintances in the Torah world in London. As a result, Chaim had two tentative offers for work in a yeshiva high school and in the Talmud Torah where Chaim's brother Ari was teaching. The *rav* also set up a telephone interview between Chaim and a *kiruv* organization called Journeys. It looked as though Chaim would be able to find meaningful employment, and meaningful employment would positively impact his state of mind. And, of course, his state of mind would definitely impact his healing.

Ari and Yaffa had done their legwork for us in the local schools and kindergartens. Yaffa coordinated a phone conversation between me and the principal of the Yesodey Hatorah School for Girls. The call was pleasant enough, but the principal could not promise to accept our girls as students before meeting us. I was not overly concerned, as Shoshi and Miri were both bright and well-behaved children. I felt they would be an asset to any class. Yaffa, herself, was a substitute teacher in the school and I believed that she would have some influence in getting our girls accepted.

As far as Yochanan was concerned, there were many available preschools and I wanted to personally check out the teachers before deciding on one. And, naturally, I wanted Yaakov at home to keep me company for the time being.

Yaffa had found us a furnished apartment, including basic kitchen utensils, close to her home in Stamford Hill, London's large religious Jewish community where she had been born. She rented it for us for two months, with the option of extending the lease. During that time, if I wished, I could look for something more suitable.

I spoke to Stephen Rivers about our imminent move and my desire to use his services. He suggested that I immediately book an appointment as there was normally a month-long wait for new clients. I set up an appointment scheduled for a month after our arrival. A shiver ran up and down my spine as I hung up the phone. This was really happening! Indirect hypnosis was now a part of our future.

I felt incredibly grateful that all the preliminary steps to our move were taken care of quite effortlessly. However, the big question was, how easily would we acclimate to a different mentality of people with a completely different daily schedule. And how could we get used to a climate that differed so dramatically from that of Eretz Yisrael? Would I find friends? Would I be able to work? Would Chaim be cured?

THE BIG DAY ARRIVES

I was both looking forward to and dreading the day of our move, but there was no stopping its arrival. It dawned with a clear sky and birds singing. If only I could feel as lighthearted as the birds did!

We were lucky to have been able to reach Rav Scheinerman the night before. He assured us that he would daven for us daily and we could feel secure in the knowledge that we were doing the right thing. He concluded with a heartfelt blessing for success for both of us. His words of caring and concern touched me deeply. They were like torches glowing in the dark of night to light my way and give me hope.

Chaim davened with the *neitz minyan,* as our minivan was coming for us at seven a.m. Joe, Mike, and Alexander all converged on our apartment in time to help us with our load of suitcases, army sacks, backpacks, and baby strollers. Irena had sent over a box full of home-baked cinnamon buns and Bassy had sent enough of her delicious tuna-salad sandwiches, granola bars, and fruit to keep us well-supplied with food for our journey. As much as I was grateful for the gifts of food, I valued the farewell letters so much more, because they were food for my soul. I saved them to read on the flight, as I wanted to savor them over and over and digest them slowly. It was so good to know that I had dear friends who truly cared for our welfare.

It took over half an hour to load the minivan but finally, we were on our way. I was able to block out the children's bickering since I was glued to the window of the van, engraving into my memory every bit of Eretz Yisrael flashing by my eyes.

At the airport, Chaim hailed a porter, who loaded our baggage onto a cart. He escorted us all the way through weigh-in. We had to pay for the excess baggage but that was just one more expense in the list of expenses our move entailed. If we could arrive in London in a calm state of mind, with everyone and everything intact, what more could I ask for?

THE FLIGHT

Chaim had taken his antianxiety medication, which often induced sleep. The less exposure he had to noise, the more secure I would feel. I had no idea how I would handle a mid-air attack and the best way to prevent one was if Chaim slept through the flight. As soon as breakfast was over, I gave him half a sleeping pill and told him to take a nap, as I needed him to have strength and energy when we arrived. He agreed and it wasn't long before he dozed off.

Since we were on a day flight and neither I nor my little ones planned on sleeping, I would have to keep them occupied for the duration of the six-hour flight. I had planned my strategy in advance and promised the children a new present every hour of the trip if they behaved nicely and played quietly. I had actually bought twenty-four different items, wrapped individually in different colored paper with their names written on each one. The colorful gift wrap roused their attention and, I believed, their motivation to behave.

The flight passed uneventfully. Chaim actually woke up on his own in time for landing and, to my great delight, was unusually calm. I decided we would wait until all the passengers had alighted so that we could avail ourselves of the stewardess' help. We spent the time waiting by my telling the children a story and they cooperated by giving me their full attention. I think even Chaim was listening and enjoying the adventure story that I was fabricating on the spot.

Unfortunately, the stewardess arrived to help us off the plane before I got to the end. The children wanted to hear how the story ended and refused to move. I had to assure them that as soon as we got into the taxi on the way to our new home, I would finish my tale. That was enough to get them moving. Happily, I was able to elicit their cooperation by offering them a treat rather than dealing with them harshly. If only I could always do that.

WELCOME TO LONDON

It took us some time to collect all of our baggage, but eventually we passed through customs and out into the visitors' lounge of the airport. We had no idea where to go, but suddenly we heard our names being called.

"Chaim! Sari! Here, over here! We're here!!"

There were Ari and Yaffa and their two children waving excitingly to us. What a good feeling to see someone familiar in the midst of strangeness.

"Yaffa! I'm so glad to see you," I exclaimed as we embraced.

"Sari! You look great! How was your trip?"

The two brothers were equally emotional as they hugged each other. The children became excited as the older ones remembered their little cousins. They interacted like friends meeting after a long separation. If the start of our trip was any indication of what our stay in London would be like, I dared to hope that we would have a good time in our new home.

Ari led us to the van he had rented for the trip. While Chaim and Ari loaded it with our baggage, Yaffa and I settled the children into their seats. Our children were so busy with their cousins that they forgot that I owed them the end of the story. Within an hour of landing we were on our way to Stamford Hill.

After having lived in Eretz Yisrael for the past few years, we had forgotten about the great distances that existed between airports and residential areas. We had certainly forgotten that so many thousands of trees could exist in a single area, or that luscious green grass could stretch for endless miles upon miles. It was a feast for the eyes.

Before long the sun disappeared behind large gray clouds and it began to drizzle.

"Where did the sun go?" Miri wanted to know. "It feels so cold!"

"Ima, I'm so glad you made us wear our winter jackets and gloves!" Shoshi said.

"Yes, children, the temperature is quite a bit cooler than what we're used to in Eretz Yisrael. But you'll get used to it quickly."

We all snuggled down into our warm coats and slowly fell silent. During the long journey, one by one the little ones nodded off into a deep sleep. As much as I tried staying awake, I too must have drifted off because the next thing I knew, we had arrived at our new home in Stamford Hill.

302 CAZENOVE PLACE

We were parked in front of an old brownstone house, with a small garden in front consisting of a lone rosebush. It had a rather dilapidated look about it. The house, at 302 Cazenove Place, belonged to Rabbi Shmuel Steiner, who rented it out, fully furnished, on a monthly or yearly basis. Through the raindrops it looked as though it were about a hundred years old. But the colorful handmade *"Beruchim Haba'im —*
Welcome to London" sign on the front door turned the house into our mansion and made us feel very welcome. I told myself that as long as it had a roof and enough beds for us all, it would be fine.

Yaffa and I transported the sleepy kids into the house while the men unloaded the van. We settled them in the front room, which faced the street. It would serve as our living room and playroom.

"Yaffa, where did these toys come from?" I was mystified by the presence of a large carton full of building blocks, dolls, stuffed animals, and toy soldiers.

"Rabbi Steiner's children no longer need them, so he brought this box over. He said you can keep them."

"That's so considerate of him!" I exclaimed. "Children, look what our landlord brought you."

Wide awake by now, they rushed over to examine the contents of the toy box. Within seconds they were immersed in their games and oblivious to us.

"The kids are busy playing, so let's go to the kitchen and get a meal together," Yaffa suggested.

"That's a good idea!" I replied enthusiastically. My stomach was grumbling, as it was late afternoon and Bassy's tuna sandwiches were long forgotten.

The night before, Yaffa had filled the pantry with basic staples and the fridge with dairy products and a cooked meal. She now heated the cooked dishes on the stovetop. Before long, we were all sitting in our kitchen enjoying a delicious "Welcome Home" meal from our dear brother and sister-in-law. It was surprising how tasty spaghetti and cheese with tangy tomato sauce could taste. I really appreciated Yaffa's thoughtfulness. It made our first moments in our new home so much more pleasurable.

Once we finished eating and washing the dishes, Yaffa gave me a tour of the house. Beyond the front room there were a few steps going down that led to the kitchen, toilet, and large dining room. From the dining room, a door led to the back garden where a sukkah could be built. Near the kitchen there were stairs leading down to a dingy basement, used as a storage area. We then went up the stairs to the first floor containing three bedrooms, a bathroom, and another toilet. I noticed that there were no showers. The older English homes used four-legged baths that looked as though they had come out of a museum. I wasn't much of a bath person, but I guessed this would be the least problematic adjustment I'd need to make in my new home.

The place was really ancient. There was another thing I could not figure out. "Yaffa, what are those funny white metal boxes hanging on the walls in the bathroom and over the sinks?"

"Open the hot water faucet and you'll find out," she answered.

I did as she instructed and was amazed at the results. These were mini hot-water boilers. When the hot-water faucet was turned on, a fire automatically lit, which heated the water in the tank rather quickly. As the hot water was used, new water flowed into the tank and was heated. That meant that one could not fill up a deep bath and expect that the water would be very hot, as only small amounts of water in the tank could be heated at one time.

As far as heating for the house, there was none, other than small heaters placed in the rooms. The halls and staircases, lacking these heaters, were notoriously cold in the winter. As it was now the end of October, the air was quite chilly. It was too bad that we didn't have a nice big fireplace in the living room of this ancient house. There actually had been a fireplace in the front room, but it was not functional and had been converted into a bookcase.

I had prepared one of the suitcases with all we needed for our first night. Chaim brought it upstairs and then went to daven *Minchah* with Ari and to buy some things at the nearby grocery and pharmacy.

Yaffa helped me put the linens on the beds and find everyone's pajamas, slippers, toothbrushes, and odds and ends. Yaakov would not go to sleep without his "blanky" nor could Miri fall asleep without her teddy bear. So we spent a good hour getting each child's paraphernalia sorted out. Yaakov would sleep in our bedroom, the other three children would share the second room, and the third would be our guest room. Yes, Joe would have a place to sleep whenever he'd come.

Yaffa wrote her phone number on a large piece of paper and scotch-taped it to the front of the fridge. It was time for her to take her little ones home.

"Sari, get to sleep early," she said at the front door. "I'm coming over in the morning to take you to the Yesodey Hatorah School for Girls for an interview with the principal. I'll be here at nine a.m.; your appointment is at nine-thirty."

"OK, Yaffa," I replied. "I'm so exhausted I think I could drop off already for the night! You're a doll for doing this! Aren't you teaching tomorrow?"

"No," she answered. "I'm off tomorrow. If the girls are accepted to the school, we'll go buy school uniforms. After that we can check out some of the preschools in the area for Yochanan. There are a few really good ones!"

We hugged and she left. I was glad that Yaffa was so highly motivated to getting us settled as soon as possible. She had undergone her own difficult adjustment period after marrying Ari and moving to B'nei Brak and so could appreciate what I was going through.

I looked at my watch. It was only five p.m. but it was already dark outside. I'd give the kids a bath and supper and then by six, which was eight p.m. Israel time, it would be off to bed for us all.

I had no idea where Chaim was and when he would come home. I called Yaffa to see if he was there. He and Ari were still out somewhere. I told her that I would leave supper on the table for Chaim as I was going to bed early.

I prepared a colorful vegetable salad and a pita filled with avocado and feta cheese for Chaim's supper. I carefully wrapped everything with plastic wrap and placed my good-night note to him on top. I still hoped he would arrive home before I fell asleep; I wanted to know how he was doing. I added a postscript to the note that he should wake me up if he needed anything.

I felt a bit anxious about how he would feel coming in to a silent home with no one to welcome him. But by this point I was struggling to keep my eyes open and I knew that the wisest thing to do was to go to sleep. Hashem knew that I had done my best for him, but now I had to take care of myself. I dropped into bed and within minutes I was in dreamland. I had survived my first day in London, and it hadn't been so bad after all.

CHAPTER NINE

Life in London

London, England, 1974

SCHOOL

J awoke early at the crack of dawn; my internal clock was still set to Israel time. I could hear the raindrops hitting the window panes. It seemed that we were in for a typical English rainy day. I remembered longingly the bright Israeli sun, blue skies, and white fluffy clouds. Oh, how I missed them already! I savored the warmth under my covers, and had no desire or willpower to move and start my day.

I pulled myself together before the *yetzer hara* could drag me down into depression. I made a decision at that very moment that I would be grateful for everything that took place no matter how different it was from what I was used to or how difficult it was to negotiate. I was here for a good purpose with the *rav's* blessings, and I would look for the silver lining in every cloud. I would treat each hurdle as a challenge — an exciting challenge. My first challenge now would be to learn how to welcome the rain as a pleasant alternative to the sweltering heat of a typical Israeli day.

I strained to hear the chirping of birds in the trees, but that lovely sound was strikingly absent. I decided to make my own lovely sounds by singing a happy tune to the words of *Modeh ani*. Next, I would get to the kitchen and put up the kettle for a delicious cup of coffee. The sound of bubbling water as it boiled would take the place of chirping birds and bring me a feeling of contentment. After all, there was so much pleasure in that piping hot cup of coffee that I loved to savor at the beginning of each day. Why take it for granted instead of letting it fill me with a good, warm, and grateful feeling.

Playing this "Appreciation Game" sounded simpler than it really was. But I determined that this would be my new way of being. "Attitude, attitude, attitude!" would become my mantra and the key to my success. Having a positive outlook on life would be the method I used, not only to "survive" living in London, but to actually enjoy being there. I started that day and never let up. My "game" became my constant companion and, I may say, helped me tremendously in discovering the silver lining in every cloud.

I was happy to see Chaim fast asleep. I had no idea when he had come home, as my exhaustion of the night before had induced a coma-like sleep, sightless and soundless, until the moment I awoke. I hoped that he had enjoyed himself with Ari and perhaps made some acquaintances in shul.

I rose quietly so as not to disturb his sleep and began my day with the new measure of motivation I had just created. I davened and then quickly prepared a healthy breakfast before waking the children. We had a long and hopefully productive day ahead of us and I wanted them to be sustained with wholesome food. Next, I needed to find everyone's boots, umbrellas, and sweaters in the suitcases. This was definitely not a simple matter. Luckily, I had a few hours to get organized before Yaffa would be ringing our doorbell.

I managed to get everyone ready by the time Yaffa arrived. She had left her children with her mother in order to be totally at my service. I, on the other hand, was taking all of my brood along, as Chaim was still in shul and had his own appointments to attend to later that day. I planned on exchanging experiences with him when we met at home for a late lunch.

Yaffa suggested that we take a minicab to the school since the rain was coming down rather heavily. There was plenty of rain, but as yet, no lightening or thunder. I felt apprehensive, remembering all too vividly Chaim's reaction to the crashing of thunder in Dr. Aarons' office. I left Chaim's anti-anxiety medication on the table next to his breakfast together with my good-bye note and prayed that he would take it.

He certainly couldn't afford to lose his self-control, as he was going for job interviews that day. Ari was accompanying him, but he didn't know about Chaim's anti-anxiety pills. I tried calling Ari before we left but there was no answer. Yaffa noticed how worried I looked.

"Sari, why don't you write another note in red marker, reminding Chaim to take his medication?"

"That's an idea, Yaffa. If I place it right on top of his breakfast, there's no way he can miss it."

I prepared the note and left it conspicuously on top of his breakfast. More than that, I could not do.

I had to relinquish control of the situation, since we never actually have control over life. It is Hashem Who puts us into situations beyond our control. Our job is to do whatever we can, our *hishtadlus*, and then to rely on Hashem's goodness for whatever outcome He chooses for us. I wanted to feel myself in Hashem's embrace and to know that whatever happened was exactly what needed to happen. And with that thought in mind, we left.

In the car, Yaffa produced funny puppets from her bag to play with Yaakov and Yochanan. This was her way of making friends with them, as she was going to be their babysitter while I was in the principal's office with the girls. Yaakov laughed delightedly at Yaffa's antics, but Yochanan remained aloof. He needed a bit more time to get comfortable with her. I had a feeling that she would win him over shortly, as she had a special way with children. Once more, I felt a rush of appreciation to Hashem for all the ways He provided to ease our transition into our new home.

At the school, we had a short wait before being ushered into the principal's office. Rebbetzin Schleisinger was an elderly woman with a kind face. I had been afraid that we would be faced with a stern-looking matron who would frighten the girls. After spending a few minutes talking with me she turned to speak to Shoshi and then Miri.

Smiling at Shoshi, she asked, "What is your name?"

"Shoshana Perlman, but everyone calls me Shoshi."

"So we will also call you Shoshi. How do you like being in England?"

"I'm very happy to see Aunt Yaffa and Uncle Ari and my cousins. But I don't know if I like the rain so much."

Rebbetzin Schleisinger tried unsuccessfully to stifle a chuckle. "Well, although it rains a lot it doesn't rain every day," she said, "and the school makes outings to the beautiful English parks on some of our sunny days."

The kind principal had succeeded in putting Shoshi at ease with her soft and attentive manner. Now she was ready to get to the business of assessing Shoshi's educational level, her maturity, and proficiency in speaking English.

"Your mother told me you're in second grade. Can you tell me what you learned in first grade and at the beginning of this school year?"

Shoshi, with her natural confidence, rattled off a long list of subjects that she had mastered in her short school career.

After spending a full ten minutes speaking with each child and seeing how well they read in Hebrew, the Rebbetzin wrote some notes in the file on her desk. This input was necessary to guide her in deciding which grade to place them in. In England, children begin the first grade of compulsory schooling at age five, unlike the USA or Eretz Yisrael where first graders are typically six years old. Shoshi had been in second grade in Eretz Yisrael but if she were put into a class of girls her age, she would find herself in the British third grade. The principal had to assess her educational level in order to decide if she should be placed with children of her own age or in a lower class.

She then turned to me. "You have lovely children, *bli ayin hara,* Mrs. Perlman. They are very bright and pleasant. They have obviously been well brought up." The Rebbetzin smiled at me as she spoke.

"Thank you," I answered simply.

"I am happy to accept them as our students. However, they will need tutoring to learn to read and write in English, and in math as well. Our children begin learning reading at age five, so yours have quite a bit of catching up to do. Until they catch up to their appropriate age levels, I will be required to place them in a class of younger children. This is no reflection on their intelligence. But it would be senseless to place them in classes where the children are reading English proficiently and yours still don't have basic reading skills. Once they have closed the gap they could be moved up into the age-appropriate class.

"On the other hand, they are at quite an advantage over our children in their knowledge of *lashon hakodesh* subjects. They might be bored in these lessons and might benefit from being in a higher class." The Rebbetzin then presented a lengthy discussion on the benefits and setbacks of my children being in a class above, with, or below their age group.

I was trying to sort out all the advantages and disadvantages in my head but was getting a bit confused.

"There seem to be so many factors here that would impact a decision. I can't even keep track of all of them," I said, somewhat chagrined.

"That's perfectly normal. You are not the first one to come to our school with this problem. Here's a list of the pros and cons I just talked about." She handed me a paper on which she'd jotted down the points as she spoke. "As you read it you will have a clearer picture of what we're dealing with."

After reading through the page, I nodded understandingly.

"I'm impressed with everything you have said. You truly care about what's best for my girls. I really appreciate that."

"What works best for the child works best for the school," the Rebbetzin said. "Everyone gains when we end up with happy students and parents instead of unhappy students and frustrated parents."

"That certainly makes sense," I said. "How does one get tutoring help? And who pays for it?"

"British citizens can get a certain amount of tutoring financed by the government. You, however, will have to pay for it out of pocket. You may be able to obtain some funding from various tzedakah organizations. The school has several excellent and reasonably priced tutors and we can arrange the meetings for you."

We had been talking for close to an hour and it was time to conclude.

"Please discuss the pros and cons with your husband. Once you have an idea of what you want to do and decide to register your girls in the school, it will be necessary for your husband to come to school and sign a tuition contract. Then, make an appointment for an RWM evaluation for each child. This will enable us to create a tutoring protocol for them."

The Rebbetzin turned to the children. "I will be very happy to have you as students here and I hope you too will be happy in our school. Thank you, girls, for being so patient while I talked to your mother."

"You're welcome!" they chorused in their politest tone of voice. She must have thought that they were little angels in human guise!

She led us to the door and wished us a good day. The interview was over and I was relieved. It was clear that we would get individualized attention for the girls in this school. Another advantage was that Yaffa was a substitute teacher in the school. Having an aunt around would help the girls integrate more easily.

I liked Rebbetzin Schleisinger immensely. Yaffa had told me that she ruled the school with firm discipline, yet she was a most intelligent and compassionate person. Discipline with understanding and flexibility was a perfect mix for a healthy educational environment. There was no need to check out any of the other girls' schools, as this one seemed to meet our needs perfectly. I felt that I had now surmounted the first hurdle on our road to settling in to our new home.

I searched the corridor for Yaffa and the boys but they were nowhere in sight. The rain had stopped and I found them in the school playground, enjoying the swings. Shoshi and Miri joined in for a few minutes of fun and laughter. Then we moved on to buy school uniforms for the girls.

The preschools were spread out over a radius of several miles. It took us over two hours to go through all of them. Each one had its pluses and minuses and so I made a list of pros and cons, like the Rebbetzin had made, in order to discuss them with Chaim. Together, we would decide which nursery seemed most suitable for Yochanan.

By this time, everyone was famished and exhausted. Besides needing food, I could see that we were all ready for an afternoon nap. We jumped into the first cab that came along and sped homeward. Yaffa declined to join us for lunch, anxious to get home.

"Yaffa, I can't thank you enough!" I said with deep emotion as we stood by the front door. "I don't know what I would have done without you!"

"Sari, don't be so dramatic! It was no big deal! I'm sure you would have done the exact same thing for me."

"Yeah, but you do it with such a bright smile on your face, with such *seiver panim yafos*. That's why your name is Yaffa, because of your *panim yafos*!"

"Sari, I give you my vote for the best wife and mother of the year!"

"What do you mean, Yaffa?" I was puzzled. "I'm just a regular wife and mother."

"No, Sari, you're not. Do you think every wife would have agreed to pick herself and her family up from her comfortable home in Eretz Yisrael and move overseas on the odd chance that maybe some hypnotist could heal her husband?"

"Of course they would!" I said adamantly. "And don't forget, the *rav* told us to go."

"Sari, I'm sure the *rav* told you to go because he knew you would do so willingly. He wouldn't have told just anyone to go, especially if she was opposed to the move."

"But what else could we have done? There were no other options."

"There are always options. Another wife would have said, 'We'll just wait around until Ericksonian Hypnosis comes to Eretz Yisrael.'"

My facial expression must have expressed my total disagreement with what she was saying. I was sure she was all mixed up, and that any wife would have done just as I did. I began to say something but she cut me off.

"Look at me, Sari. I wanted London and Ari wanted B'nei Brak. And I persuaded him to come here. I wasn't able to do what you did — follow your husband to wherever he wanted to be."

"Yaffa, you were homesick! If I would have been homesick for America, I probably also would have gone back. But I wanted to stay in Eretz Yisrael."

"Are you homesick for Eretz Yisrael now?" she asked me. "Are you going to be running back home before Chaim gets his cure?"

I *was* homesick for Eretz Yisrael. But it never occurred to me that one could give up on one's goals that easily. It seemed natural to me that one persevered until the very end. I couldn't say this to Yaffa, as she felt that she had succumbed to her challenge. I needed to raise her self-esteem somehow. I suddenly had a brainstorm.

"Yaffa, you know why you decided to come back to London? It was because you needed to be here to help us! Hashem used you as the tool for fulfilling our needs. Something like why Yosef was sold to Mitzrayim."

"OK, Rebbetzin Sarah! We're both great and we both have to learn from each other. Now you eat something quickly and go for a nice nap together with the kids."

We hugged and she left. I took her advice and did just as she had instructed. Before I fell asleep I wondered how Chaim was doing. I had no idea where he was.

CHAIM'S DAY

I slept deeply until I heard the front door slam shut. I pulled my eyelids open (they felt stuck together) and looked at my watch. It was four in the afternoon.

"Chaim," I called, "is that you?"

"Yes, Sari." He entered the bedroom. His face was shining. "What a day I had! Everyone I spoke to received me with open arms. They all seemed so eager to have me join their staff."

"That's wonderful!" I exclaimed. "Hashem is really on our side!"

"I don't get it!" he continued. "They don't know me, never heard me teach or give a *shiur*, or talk to people on the phone, or organize an event. How could they be so positive about me? It doesn't make sense."

"Maybe you made a really good impression on them? Maybe they could sense what a great asset you'd be working for them. You have great references!"

I let those words sink in before I continued. But I could see his mind was focused elsewhere and wasn't even sure that he heard me. I doggedly continued, trying to encourage him. "Maybe Rav Scheinerman's *tefillos* are helping us. Maybe he really implored his friends to hire you...Or Hashem wants us to have it easy here. Maybe you deserve to have it easy here. What if it means that we'll be very successful here and be able to return home real soon? *Yeshu'as Hashem k'heref ayin* — the salvation of Hashem is like the blink of an eye!"[17]

A long moment of silence passed. He then slowly regained his focus as he looked at me and suddenly smiled.

"Let's have something to eat. I'm starving! And then I'll tell you everything that happened today."

I jumped out of bed, happy for the fact that the children were still sleeping. It had been a long time since Chaim and I had sat down together quietly without having our to-do lists in our hands or in our minds. It was so important to share some private time together, share our concerns, worries, and, more importantly, our triumphs, in a slow and relaxed manner.

I wasn't very hungry but determined to eat something together with Chaim. I quickly prepared scrambled eggs and a fresh salad and put whole-wheat bagels in the toaster. Chaim was ravenous and ate quickly. Then, over hot cups of cocoa, he told me about the events of his day.

"The first interview was at Yeshivas Darkei Aharon, a *yeshiva ketanah* for fourteen- to sixteen-year-old boys. The Rosh Yeshiva, Rabbi Mordechai Rosenbaum, is quite a *talmid chacham* himself. He needs a *rebbi* for the sixteen-year-olds, as his current *rebbi* is ill and wishes to retire as soon as a replacement is found. The job entails being at the yeshiva at seven-thirty a.m. for *tefillas Shacharis* and then, after breakfast, teaching till twelve noon. I'd have to give two separate *shiurim* daily from Sunday through Thursday. I would be free to use my afternoons for my personal learning and for preparing my *shiurim* for yeshiva.

"The second interview was at Yeshivas Yesodey Hatorah Boys School, where Ari teaches. The boys range from five years to bar mitzvah. The principal, Rabbi Shaul Shurkin, is a friendly fellow. He needs someone to be available as a substitute teacher for any of his classes, and someone who can tutor boys in the afternoons. I'd have to be in the school from one p.m. till six p.m. for the tutoring, and be available every morning, Sunday through Friday, in case he needs me. He's willing to give me a reasonable salary, since by keeping myself available in the mornings, I'd be unable to work somewhere else. This job entails almost no preparation, and I'd have plenty of free time for my own learning, but it's definitely less challenging than the first."

I nodded in agreement and waited for Chaim to continue.

"The last stop was at the *kiruv* organization called Journeys. It is a branch of the Israeli Yad L'Achim. My duties there would entail making phone calls, mostly at night, and helping with organizing weekends. They might also need me as a learning partner for new *baalei teshuvah* and for me to come along on the weekend retreats. My salary would be paid in accordance with the hours of work I put in. The advantage with this job is that I could put in as many hours of work as I feel able to.

"What do you think, Sari?" Chaim asked me.

I had a feeling that he knew what he wanted to do, but I was curious to see if we were actually thinking along the same lines. I also wanted to use this opportunity to boost his ego.

"Chaim, with all of your abilities and experience I feel you would be most fulfilled teaching the sixteen-year-old boys. I know it means putting in a lot of preparation time, but your talent would be wasted as a substitute teacher or a tutor for little boys. I also like the idea that your free afternoons would leave you time for hypnotherapy. And if we needed additional income, you would still have the evenings to put in some hours for the *kiruv* organization. What would you like to do?"

"I feel really excited about teaching in Yeshivas Darkei Aharon," he said enthusiastically. "Rabbi Rosenbaum came across as a very special person. He told me that he had been a close acquaintance of Rav Scheinerman during the time he learned in Eretz Yisrael, and had even been his *chavrusa* for two years. He gives a *chaburah* in the evenings, and once we're settled in I'd really love to join.

"I also met some of the other *rebbei'im* and they impressed me as serious, upright people, people I'd like to spend my time with. Rav Scheinerman really knew where to send me. I feel it would be a great place for me to work in. The pay is less than what I'd get in

Yeshivas Yesodey Hatorah, but the gain is in the Torah learning I'd be investing in to prepare my classes and the satisfaction I'd get from the teaching.

"Journeys sounds like a good place too, but I couldn't start there yet. I'd have to get used to my teaching schedule and first see how many hours of prep time I need before I could take on another job. But I think between the Darkei Aharon salary and you giving some classes or doing photography we could make ends meet. How does that sound to you?"

"It sounds great! Between your adventures and mine I can't believe that all this happened in one day. It's just too good to be true! Thank you, Hashem for making things work out so well!"

"Chaim," I added, "is there anything else you have to know about the job? Like, do they pay the salaries on time, do they have money for heating in the winter, are the boys regular, normal boys, or maybe they are learning disabled, or I don't know what else might be a problem." I didn't know what was making me feel apprehensive. Perhaps I was thinking that "this great job" really was too good to be true.

"I'm surprised at you, Sari!" Chaim exclaimed. "Now look at who's being negative. What in the world is making you say that?"

"I don't know. But *yeshivos* often have money troubles. Maybe you should speak to someone who works there."

"Well, if it will make you happy, I took the phone number of one of the *rebbei'im* I met today and I can ask him about the work conditions. His name is Reb Chatzkel Stefansky. He told me he gets home at six p.m. every day. I'll call him when I get back from *Minchah-Ma'ariv*."

"Thanks, Chaim. I'm sure he'll tell you only good things about the yeshiva but I think it makes sense to speak to someone who knows the yeshiva from the inside out. My mother always taught me that it's better to be safe than sorry."

It was some instinct of mine that made me speak this way.

Normally, I am not a pessimist or an overly cautious person. But something was pushing me to take these precautions.

Chaim helped me clear the table and wash up. Just in time, too; suddenly we heard Yaakov wailing. His cries roused the others and before we knew it, we had all four of them on our laps. We spent some fun time together and then Chaim left for shul.

REB CHATZKEL AND MALKY STEFANSKY

As he had promised, as soon as Chaim got home he called Reb Chatzkel Stefansky. To our great amazement, he was clearly one of the most unbelievable people we had ever met. He not only answered all of Chaim's questions carefully and thoroughly, without belittling any of them as silly, but insisted that we all come over for supper. He said that it would be his and his wife's greatest pleasure to get to know us and to help us settle in. Chaim felt uncomfortable refusing and asked for directions to their home. Immediately, Reb Chatzkel said he would give us a lift in his car.

In a short while we were seated around their dining room table together with the members of the Stefansky family. Each one of them expressed kindliness in their own, age-appropriate way. It was obvious that this personality trait was of critical importance to them and that the parents had inculcated it into the behavior of the children until it was second nature.

Reb Chatzkel appeared to be in his early forties and Malky was maybe ten years older than I, about thirty-nine. The eldest Stefansky boy was away at yeshiva and the five children present ranged in age from two teenaged daughters to a little boy of three years. Although the boys of the family learned in Chassidic institutions, the girls learned in Yesodey Hatorah School for Girls. One of them, a second-grader, would most likely be in a class with Shoshi, but she assured Miri that they could play together during recess.

The supper was definitely a great hit. This loving family, who acted as though their greatest pleasure in life was in helping us out, made us realize how truly united Am Yisrael was in trying to ease the plight of a fellow Jew. I hoped I would be able to take this lesson of love and caring with me as I traveled through life.

I now understood what had caused me to be so cautious about Chaim taking the job with Yeshivas Darkei Aharon. Hashem obviously wanted us to meet the Stefansky family early on, in order to sweeten our time in this foreign land and make our transition as easy as possible.

Once supper was over the men moved off to Reb Chatzkel's study, the children ran off to the playroom, and I had some quiet time, albeit with Yaakov on my lap, getting to know my hostess.

"What a sweet baby!" Malky said. "Are you going to enroll him in a playgroup?"

"Definitely not! I want to keep him at home for as long as I can. He is a baby for such a tiny part of his life and I want to enjoy this special time with him while I can. The little ones grow up so quickly, almost before we realize it."

"I feel just the same. If a mother isn't working and has the option, she should be her baby's caretaker. Why give the job to someone else?"

"Exactly so! Do you work, Malky?"

"No, I'm a full-time wife and mother. And I happen to have lots of free time in the mornings to take you shopping whenever you want, as I have the car during the hours my husband is in yeshiva. And on the non-shopping days I have plenty of extra time before the children come home from school at four to take you on visits to the prenatal clinic and to wherever you have to go to take care of things."

I couldn't believe what I was hearing. Malky was the ultimate in kindness. I wondered how it was possible for a mother of a large family to have so much free time. It was a trick I would have to learn from her. Maybe this was another good reason for our coming to London! Was this the silver lining of the cloud?

"Malky, I'm amazed at your generous offer, especially of your time. Sometimes time is the most difficult commodity to give away."

"You're making it out to be much more than it is. Don't forget that when you shop I do my shopping at the same time."

"In that case, I would appreciate doing Shabbos shopping with you on Wednesdays." I knew that Yaffa was teaching that day, and I needed to become familiar with the kosher shops and the best places to buy.

"That's my Shabbos shopping day too. Is ten o'clock a good time?"

"Perfect."

"I'll teach you the ins and outs of the local shops. Maybe we should also check up on Yochanan in his playgroup to be sure that he's doing well. If he isn't, we can simply take him along with us on our shopping spree."

Wow, I thought, *life is really flowing along smoothly!* I felt like I was in some kind of dream world.

Malky was a wise and perceptive woman. I realized this when she said, "You know, Sari, I have a few free hours tomorrow and I'd love to help you unpack. How about if you give me a call tomorrow to let me know when it's a good time for you?"

I was suddenly jolted into reality. I had totally forgotten that besides digging out a few sweaters and pairs of boots, I still had fifteen pieces of luggage to unpack. A whole day had flown by almost magically, and I hadn't done a thing to get settled in. How did Malky know that I had to unpack? She had probably assumed that, after hearing how I had spent my day, I had simply never gotten around to doing it. How right she was! Her offer was more than generous. It was a gift of gold and I readily agreed.

"I have to go with Chaim to Yesodey Hatorah to sign a tuition contract and then get Yochanan settled in preschool, so I'm not sure when I'll be home. But I'll keep your wonderful offer in mind and call you when I can."

"Good. And if it doesn't work out by day then maybe it will at night after the children are in bed. And if not tomorrow then maybe after shopping on Wednesday we can tackle a few suitcases. But we have to get you unpacked by Shabbos!"

"Malky, you are unbelievable!" I felt shy expressing my feelings, but I had to let her know how grateful I was. "How are you able to be so sensitive to another person's needs?"

She laughed. "It's nothing really. It's just obvious, isn't it? Anyone would realize that you need to get unpacked and learn where to shop. And we want you to feel welcome in Stamford Hill!"

She almost convinced me that it was nothing. That was her greatness, her ability to downplay everything she did. But I wouldn't get confused, and I would remember her kindness forever.

I started then to realize that Malky was the type of person who had to find a solution to every problem; someone who never took no for an answer. But she did it in such a gentle way, without nervousness or stubbornness. I certainly had a lot to learn from her.

Although we only lived three blocks away from where they lived, Reb Chatzkel insisted on driving us home. The children were thoroughly happy with their new friends as I was with mine. I had a feeling that Malky would also be instrumental in helping me set up my photography studio and my childbirth classes. Somehow, she seemed to be a person who was able to do everything. I had yet to learn what else this incredible woman was dealing with in her life.

THE FIRST MONTH

I can't claim unequivocally that every day was a bed of roses or a bowl of cherries or whatever else they say when things are rolling along fantastically. We had our good days and our bad days. There were days when Miri refused to go to school. She often didn't understand what the girls were saying in their British accent and found it hard making friends with her classmates. Normally, she was the happy-go-lucky kid in the family, but her insecurity in school affected her friendly nature. To our good luck, having her aunt and the

Stefansky girl to talk to and socialize with during recess helped her to finally adjust to her own classmates.

Shoshi had her own issues. She felt ashamed of being in a class with girls younger than her, as she had always been at the top of her class. As much as we explained to her why she had to temporarily be with younger kids, she still felt mortified. She was convinced that she stuck out like a sore thumb.

"Shoshi, do you remember the story of Rabbi Akiva?" I asked her one day. She looked at me inquisitively.

"Rabbi Akiva was one of our greatest *talmidei chachamim*. But did you know that when he first began to learn to read he was forty years old in a class of three- and four-year-old little boys? You can be sure that he stuck out like a sore thumb, but he stayed in that class until he learned what he had to learn. And then he moved on, step-by-step, to higher and higher classes, and higher and higher levels. That is how he was able to become one of the greatest teachers of Torah to Am Yisrael. But it all started because he decided he must learn the *aleph-beis* even if it meant sitting in class with tiny children."

That story finally enabled her to calm down and become accepting of the situation. Once she relaxed her learning accelerated and, over time, she was to become a student at the head of her class, even in London.

On top of all that, Yochanan cried every time I left him at nursery. I could only leave him for a short time each day. It took him several weeks until he slowly adjusted to the children and to his teacher. Eventually, he loved his playgroup, but it took a fair share of my time and my strength getting him there.

I was quite concerned during this adjustment period, because I was anxious for Chaim to start hypnotherapy as planned. I certainly didn't want to cancel our appointment. I knew that the sooner we started, the sooner we would reach our end point. And we could only begin sessions if I knew that the children were happy during school hours. I could not sacrifice their well-being even for the lofty goal of getting Chaim well.

But Hashem was merely testing my faith in "all that He does is for the best." It must have been His way of building up my endurance, resilience, and my patience. But suddenly, as though a switch had been thrown, the children were going happily to school and Yaakov was playing with Malky's three-year-old like the best of friends.

Malky agreed for me to leave Yaakov with her on the afternoons that Chaim and I went for hypnosis sessions, and even have the older ones come to her in case we were late getting home. This was a perfect arrangement, as Yaffa was not always free on the days of our appointments. The children loved going to Malky and I knew that she loved having them. To her every opportunity of doing a mitzvah was a privilege rather than a burden. I had a lot to learn from her.

Another concern of ours was the high noise level in the yeshiva. If one were not familiar with the yeshiva scene, he might mistakenly think that a screaming match was going on inside the walls of the institution. When Chaim started teaching again in Yeshivas Shaarei Orah, Rabbi Reichman wisely instructed the boys to keep their decibel levels low during the hours Chaim was present. This ploy worked fairly well. But in Yeshivas Darkei Aharon, no such precaution was being taken for the new *rebbi* suffering from hyperacusis. I was always fearful that Chaim might have an attack while in the yeshiva. But *baruch Hashem*, it never happened. Before we left Eretz Yisrael, Rav Scheinerman had blessed him that in the merit of his learning and teaching Torah, Chaim would have the ability to control his panicky feelings that often preceded an attack.

Chaim's love of learning and his intense focus during teaching enabled him to stay in control. He told me that on several occasions he felt an attack was imminent, but he maintained control until he was able to get to the restrooms, splash his face with cold water, and breathe deeply until the feeling passed. However, this did not mean that outside the protective atmosphere within the yeshiva walls he was free of his debilitating attacks.

THE FIRST HYPNOSIS SESSION

There were so many "firsts" in my life, and the day when we would meet Stephen Rivers for the first time arrived, bringing with it a feeling of both excitement and trepidation. He was the reason for our having uprooted ourselves from our wonderful home in B'nei Brak. He was what we were pinning our hopes on for Chaim's healing. Of course, all healing comes from Hashem, but we needed a messenger to act as a conduit for that healing to flow into our lives. Was Stephen Rivers the right messenger? I silently prayed to Hashem to make this the last stop in our quest for healing.

We traveled on the underground railway system quite easily, as the routes were clearly printed on the transportation maps and in every train carriage. The ride took over an hour and we allotted ourselves an extra half hour for walking to the Ericksonian Hypnosis Center at 23 Harley Street. The weather was fair and visiting the city was interesting. We enjoyed our leisurely walk from the train station to our destination.

I had my camera with me. London was a two-thousand-year-old city and some of her buildings were literal antiques. The old-style architecture made me feel transported back in time and I wanted to capture a taste of the past on film. I annoyed Chaim by stopping every few feet to snap another photo of yet another house.

"Sari, come on! What's so interesting about a building! It's just a different variation of the one you snapped before!"

"Patience, patience, Chaim! When you see my London album, you'll enjoy the shots as much as I do!"

"You know what's really interesting, Sari? Those double-decker buses. Let's ride one on the way back to the train station."

"Sure, Chaim. I'd love to, especially if we sit on the upper deck."

The weather was "nice" for London, rainless for a change. The crisp air invigorated me as we walked, but I could barely feel the warmth of the weak sun on my face. I felt propelled forward, as every step was purposeful and took us closer to a place of hope. The rhythmic sound of my boots on the cobbled road, interspersed with the clicking of the camera shutter, calmed my turbulent thoughts. We were on an adventure, and no matter what the outcome, it would bring us closer to our goal.

The professional building at 23 Harley Street was quite imposing. There were many offices of doctors, lawyers, and what-nots. I searched the directory for several moments before discovering the Ericksonian Hypnosis Center on the fifth floor. The old-fashioned-looking elevator seemed rather fragile but within a few minutes we were standing at the reception desk of Stephen Rivers' office. We had arrived twelve minutes before our scheduled appointment.

The receptionist, a very efficient looking young woman by the name of Susan, handed us a form to fill out. I could feel Chaim's tension rising as, once again, he was thrust into having to deal with his infirmity.

He finished writing and I tried making small talk with Chaim, but he wasn't very responsive. He was too immersed in his memories. I continued talking, as I wanted to distract him from his past and get him to focus on the present. I reminded him that Rav Scheinerman had suggested that we try Stephen Rivers, and we should have faith that Hashem would enable him to help. He said nothing, and didn't even look at me.

I needed a new tactic in order to jolt him out of his thoughts.

"Chaim," I said suddenly. "Do you think I will have a London baby or maybe we'll be back in Eretz Yisrael before the due date?"

He turned his head and stared at me intently. That question got him to focus on me, finally!

"I...I don't know. I didn't really think about it."

"You know, Chaim, getting the children settled in school has taken so much of my time that I never had a chance to settle in myself. I haven't even seen a doctor yet or registered in any hospital."

"How do you know which hospital to register in?" Chaim asked.

"Malky has been begging to take me to the City of London Hospital where she goes for her prenatal checkups. Many of the religious women give birth there and she herself is very satisfied. I promised that at the first opportunity I would go with her when she goes. But...."

"You really should, Sari," he interjected. "You remember how sick you were last time. I'm sure you don't want a repeat of that!"

"Chaim, I'm trying my best! I can't be with Yochanan in kindergarten and at the City of London Hospital at the same time."

"OK, I know you're doing more than one woman is expected to do. But I want you to find a way to get to the hospital when Malky goes for her next appointment. Can you manage that?"

Before I could answer, Stephen Rivers exited his office and walked toward us, extending his hand as he approached. Chaim stood up to shake it.

"Welcome to London!" Stephen called out in a lively voice. He was quite the gentleman, friendly and proper at the same time. His dress, however, was rather informal, and his blond hair had a slightly wild look to it. His accent was that of an Englishman, but his mannerisms were definitely not British. It was an interesting mix.

"How are you enjoying our weather? Or should I ask, how badly are you missing the Israeli sun?"

We both laughed. "It hasn't been too bad yet," Chaim replied. "Does it get much worse?"

"I wouldn't call the weather good or bad. Rain is a friend of the earth. We have the right amount of rain and sun to keep our grass green and our roses blooming. And it never gets really cold in the winter or too hot in the summer. So why complain?" He began leading us toward the office.

I liked his answer. He was looking at the bright side of things, almost like a *dan l'chaf zechus* for the English weather that people always complained about. If he could do that with the weather, he was probably an expert at doing so with the difficulties of life.

Stephen's office was furnished in a style diametrically opposed to that of Dr. Aarons. It had a Far Eastern touch to it. I reminded myself that he had lived in many lands over the years studying various healing modalities. I wondered how all that blended in with Ericksonian hypnosis.

"Please sit down." He pointed to a comfortable armchair for Chaim and another one on the side for me. "Call me Stephen. No doctor or mister, please. What shall I call you?" he asked Chaim.

"Chaim is fine."

"Do you want your wife to remain in the room during our session?"

"Yes, at least this time."

"No problem, Chaim."

He then turned to me with a smile. "And how shall I address you?"

"Mrs. Perlman, please." I knew it was best not to have him call me by my first name, although this response must have sounded archaic to him.

"Sure, that's fine." He turned back to Chaim. "Tell me, Chaim, what do you like about Israel? I was never there myself."

I wasn't expecting that question. I figured it must be in order to get Chaim relaxed and to bring the hypnosis into play in a very conversational type of way. Talking about his problem would definitely make him tense.

They carried on a short conversation for several minutes about the land of Israel. When he felt that Chaim was sufficiently at his ease he asked more directly about his issue.

"I've had a number of conversations by phone, both with you and with Mrs. Perlman. I've heard in quite some detail what you've been through. However, I'd like you to tell me now again, shortly, what brings you all the way from Israel to see me?"

Chaim hesitated for a moment, and then said very simply, "I was in an accident that caused a serious head injury, and now I keep having these attacks. It seems that certain noises trigger them. When I get triggered I lose control and I scream or rant and maybe throw things.

I don't really remember them well, so I can't give you more details. I tried all kinds of therapy and direct hypnosis in Israel but the treatments weren't successful. So we decided to try indirect hypnosis."

"When you have an attack, does it remind you of anything?"

"What do you mean?" Chaim asked.

"Does it bring to mind a similar situation that you were in, in the past?"

Chaim sat thinking deeply with his brow furrowed. After a minute of silence, Stephen began speaking.

"You don't have to try so hard to remember. Your subconscious will give you the information when the time is right and if it is in your best interest to do so. Your subconscious mind is out to protect you. It does what it feels is best for you in the moment."

"How can that be? Can it make decisions on its own?" Chaim had asked the same questions of Dr. Aarons, and now he was interested in hearing Stephen's answer.

"There is a wisdom that has been implanted in your body by your Creator. Just as your immune system has to decide when to attack a virus and when to leave your food molecules alone, your body is making all kinds of decisions all the time. Many of these decisions are taking place in your subconscious mind, which sends out messages to the various systems in your body. And those systems respond to the messages they receive, like raising or lowering your blood pressure, for example."

"I hear what you're saying. But what does this have to do with my terror attacks?"

"Your subconscious mind is always working for you and for your benefit. Now, it seems that it has learned to react in a certain way to a trigger in the past. It may have been useful at the time this pattern began, but today this reaction is no longer useful. Sometimes it is important to update your subconscious mind with new and relevant information in order for it to learn a new and better reaction."

Chaim nodded his head in understanding. He waited for Stephen to continue.

"This actually reminds me of a similar situation with one of my clients by the name of Thomas. He was taking a cruise on an ocean liner with his family when...."

Stephen embarked on a long story about Thomas. I could not for the life of me understand what he was doing until I reminded myself of something I had read about Dr. Milton Erickson. He would tell his patients stories about someone else, but, in essence, he was directing his talk to the subconscious mind of his patient and beginning the therapy in this roundabout or indirect way. Erickson was famous for his "My friend John" method of therapy.

Meanwhile, I could see how Stephen's talk was slowly lulling Chaim into a hypnotic state. It didn't take but a few minutes for Chaim's eyes to close without a word of prompting from the hypnotist. He worked slowly, making sure that his subject was with him every step of the way. To my great surprise, there was no resistance coming from Chaim. Stephen was leading him along as though he was a little child holding on to his father's hand.

I myself was nearly hypnotized by Stephen's soothing voice, and in truth I could not remember a fraction of what he said or did. Before I knew what was happening, Chaim was talking about how he had been mistakenly locked into his classroom after everyone had left the school building when he was a small boy. He cried, screamed, threw things at the door and at the window, and inadvertently set off the alarm system. After the alarm had blared for an inestimable amount of time, the janitor came to see what was going on. Only then was he finally released.

Stephen very skillfully helped Chaim realize that as a little boy he'd had no choice but to scream, cry, and throw things in order to get someone's attention to free him. At that time, his response was perfectly understandable and the best he could possible do for himself. But now as an adult he had numerous options for helping himself.

"Chaim," Stephen asked in his hypnotic voice, "if you were in the little boy's situation today, what would you do to get out?"

Chaim took his time before answering. "I'd write a letter for help and drop it out of the window; I'd use my penknife to pick the lock open; I'd call the janitor by name loudly to attract his attention."

With gentle coaxing Stephen got Chaim to figure out another few options.

"That's wonderful, Chaim!" Stephen said in a most mesmerizing voice. "You see how creative you are in figuring out how to help yourself…Even if rescue were to turn up the next day you never need to feel despair…or helpless…because your wonderful mind is always working for you.…

"I'd like you to go, now, to the little boy locked in the classroom and help him out. Are you willing to do that for him?"

"Yes."

"See yourself there, now, Chaim…Nod your head to let me know when you are there in the classroom."

Chaim nodded his head.

"Chaim, is the little boy very frightened?"

"Yes."

"What is frightening him the most?"

"He feels very helpless…" Chaim was speaking very quietly and very slowly, typical for someone in a deep trance. "He's afraid he will never get out…But that loud noise is scaring him too, that crazy loud noise!"

"Do you mean the alarm noise, the burglar alarm?"

"Yes!"

"Chaim, why did the school put in the alarm system? What did they need it for?"

"To warn people about burglars."

"Is that a good thing, Chaim?"

Chaim was quiet for a moment. "I guess so," he finally said.

"Wasn't it because of the noise of the alarm that the janitor found the little boy?"

"Yes…Yes, that's why the janitor came."

"So, Chaim, we can really say thank you to the alarm noise for bringing the janitor, can't we?" Stephen spoke slowly and deliberately. "Yes."

"I'd like you to go over to the little boy now and tell him he is no longer alone and you are going to help him."

Stephen waited for a minute to allow Chaim in his mind's eye to do as Stephen instructed him.

"Is the little boy happy you came to help him?"

"Yes."

"I'd like you to please tell the little boy that he no longer has to be afraid...He will soon be able to leave the classroom...Tell him that the big noise that is scaring him...is calling the janitor to come...to let him out of the locked classroom."

Again, Stephen waited for Chaim to carry out his instructions in the privacy of his mind. After waiting in silence for several moments, he continued speaking.

"Chaim, tell the little boy that the noise has to be very loud...otherwise the janitor might not hear it...and he wouldn't come. The reason he is coming...is because the noise is so loud...Tell the little boy...that he should be happy...that the noise is so loud...and that's why the janitor is coming...."

Again, Stephen waited in silence for an appropriate amount of time.

"What did the little boy say to you Chaim...after you explained to him why the noise needs to be so loud?"

"He said he is happy that the noise is so loud and that the janitor will now come."

"Yes, little boy...sometimes there has to be loud noises, burglar alarms, or sirens, or ambulance sirens, or police sirens, for things to happen...for good things to happen...Chaim, let me know when the janitor comes...."

After a short pause, "He's here!"

"Good, very good...Did he turn off the alarm?"

"Yes, it's quiet now..."

"Chaim," Stephen said, "tell the little boy to thank the janitor…for turning on the alarm system…when it needs to be on…and for turning off the alarm system when it needs to be off…."

Stephen was silent again for a short while.

"Tell the little boy…that whenever he hears a loud noise…that frightens him…you will come and calm him down…Are you willing to do that for him…?"

Chaim nodded his head.

"Good! Very good! When will you start doing that for him?"

"From this moment."

"What will you do, Chaim?" Stephen asked. He wanted to make sure that Chaim knew what he was meant to do.

"Whenever the little boy is afraid of a loud noise…I will come and tell him…why he does not need to be afraid…and why the loud noise is good."

"That's right…Very good, Chaim…Perfect…You did a grand job…." Stephen let his words sink in.

"Now, say goodbye to the little boy…and remind him…that you will come whenever there is a loud noise that frightens him…."

Chaim replied rather quickly, "He doesn't want me to go."

"Promise him that you will come whenever he calls you…Maybe you can give him a whistle or another way of calling you when he needs you…Do that now, Chaim…give him some way of calling you whenever he wants…Tell him he needs to go home now…They are waiting for him at home…."

Stephen allowed a short pause. "Did he go home?"

"Yes."

"Did you give him some way of calling you?"

"Yes."

"Very good, now he doesn't have to be afraid any more…not of loud noises…and not of other things unless there is a real danger…Are you happy, Chaim…that you can help him in this way?"

"Yes, very happy."

Stephen then proceeded to tell several short stories. Most likely they were meant to be metaphors with hidden messages. He concluded with suggestions that implied that Chaim would not remember consciously what had taken place but his subconscious mind would retain all that was important for it to retain. He also added that the next time he went into hypnosis, the journey would be shorter and more easily accomplished. And he repeated for emphasis that each time he went into hypnosis, the easier it would be to access. After several minutes, he brought Chaim out of his trance.

Chaim blinked his eyes and stretched his body in different directions. When he focused his eyes on Stephen, the hypnotist began speaking.

"So tell me, Chaim, which beaches in Israel do you suggest I visit when I get there?"

Stephen was talking about the subject they had been discussing a short while before Chaim had gone into hypnosis. I recognized this as a technique for creating amnesia in the patient so that he would forget what had taken place in between those two conversations.

"I love the beaches in Netanya and Hertzliya. You will also want to visit the Sea of Galilee and the Banyas River and waterfall." Chaim was acting as though the conversation about Israel had just started moments before.

Stephen carried on small talk with Chaim for another short while. Chaim never referred to what had taken place in the session.

"Well, Chaim, I'm certainly glad you made it here. I'm sure that we can find a solution to your issue. I have a feeling that you will begin feeling better really quickly." Stephen stood up.

"Aren't we going to do some hypnosis today?" Chaim acted very surprised. I had a hard time keeping myself from laughing.

"It was very important for me to get to know you first. I believe that just by coming into my office you will begin seeing change. Please have a drink of water." He handed him a glass of water. "It's important to drink water after coming here. I know it's not as tasty as Banyas water, but still...." They both laughed and I joined in, as doing so allowed me to let go of the laugh that was threatening to burst forth against my will.

Chaim drank his glass and then looked at his watch. He let out an exclamation of surprise. "What! Is this the right time? What time is it?" he looked at Stephen.

"Yes, don't worry. Your watch is right. Time seems to fly by mysteriously in this place. We really enjoyed talking about Israel but, believe it or not, it was very therapeutic."

He led us into the front office where Chaim took care of payment and set up another appointment. During that time, Stephen let me know that I was not to discuss with Chaim what had gone on in the session. If I wanted a more in-depth explanation, I could call him later that evening.

POST SESSION

As we walked toward the bus stop, we talked about Stephen and his method of working. I was relieved to hear that Chaim actually liked his new therapist. He expressed his disappointment at not having experienced hypnosis with him. I was tempted to say, "You did!" but controlled myself. I knew that indirect hypnosis had its unique ways and means of bringing about results and we had gotten a taste of that in the first session.

"What did he do, Sari? How is it possible that an hour passed when it felt to me like only ten minutes?" Chaim was really bewildered.

I was in a dilemma. It was wrong to lie, but I knew that talking about what had taken place was also wrong. For some reason, it went counter to the way Stephen worked. I begged for Heavenly help. Suddenly the words popped into my mind.

"You know, Chaim, the strangest thing happened. I can't remember a fraction of what he said. I think I was in trance myself!"

This was perfectly true. Although I heard more than Chaim did, I still could not remember a big part of what Stephen had said.

"You mean to say that I was in trance? I don't remember that at all!"

"It seems so. Otherwise, how do you explain that a whole hour passed? He must have been talking to your subconscious mind some of the time, and that's the part you can't remember."

"So who knows what he said or did during that time? Who knows what kind of suggestions he put into my mind?!" Chaim sounded quite alarmed.

"Look, Chaim, Stephen Rivers is a famous hypnotherapist and has helped hundreds if not thousands of people over the years. Rav Scheinerman felt he was a good *shaliach* and that is the main reason for our decision to use his services. We have to daven to Hashem that he should be successful and trust that his techniques are going to help you, whether or not we know exactly what he's doing. After all, every time a doctor gives you a medicine, do you check it out in a lab to see if it safe for you to take? No, you take the medication on faith that the doctor knows what he is doing.

"What it boils down to is this: If you will begin to feel positive changes you'll know that Stephen Rivers has done something right. And if not, we'll give the therapy a chance to work for a certain amount of time and then if nothing happens, we'll stop coming. It's that simple. Besides I was in the room the whole time. I would have heard if he gave any suggestions that weren't for your benefit."

Chaim mulled over my words silently; he finally looked at me with a relieved expression on his face.

"You're absolutely right! How arrogant of me to think that I have to understand exactly what's going on! Imagine if I would have questioned Dr. Tannenbaum's every move and decision. I probably wouldn't be here today!

"Come on, Sari! Let's take our 'double-decker' bus ride and enjoy ourselves." Chaim suddenly sounded like an excited child.

"I want you to snap a picture of me as I get onto the bus."

He seemed transformed and I wondered if it had anything to do with Stephen River's therapy.

CONTINUED THERAPY

We continued seeing Stephen weekly for several months. In truth, this amazing hypnotist had done the bulk of the healing in that first session. Chaim's traumatic school experience as a young child had been stored in his subconscious mind all these years. As the fear of the child within vanished, the old triggers would no longer cause the old reactions; the new reaction had been established. Essentially, Chaim was healed from his past trauma and the attacks that resulted from them. He actually hadn't had a single attack during the ensuing months of therapy.

One reason for our continuing the therapy was to provide repetition. Repetition was the key to strengthening the new neural pathways and new habit formation in the brain. Without repetition, the patient might revert to the old patterns and habits. Additionally, Stephen wanted to uncover any other episodes of a similar traumatic nature in Chaim's life that needed to be dealt with. If left in place within his memory, the old episodes could undermine the new process. As each old trauma of the past was reframed and neutralized, it would no longer affect Chaim's behavior in the present. It was like putting away old movies on the shelf in the library instead of viewing them repeatedly. In this way, their effect on him would dissipate and be forgotten.

To our great surprise, in subsequent sessions Stephen discovered three old traumas that reinforced the pattern of screaming and flailing as its response.

In a deep state of hypnosis, Stephen asked Chaim's subconscious mind to bring him back to a time when he felt helpless, to a time when he behaved in a similar fashion to the little boy locked in the classroom.

Chaim was silent for a long moment. Then he began speaking slowly. "I'm in a small boat on the sea...There's a fierce thunderstorm...The waves are gigantic...The boat is rocking wildly."

"How old are you?" Stephen asked.

"Fifteen, sixteen."

"Is someone with you?"

"I'm alone."

"What's happening?"

"The boat is filling with water. It's tipping crazily...It's overturning!" he shouted in a voice filled with fear.

"What are you doing? How are you saving yourself?" Stephen asked.

"I'm hanging on to a piece of wood." Chaim's voice was raspy and it was hard for him to speak.

"I'm kicking, kicking to stay above water...screaming...screaming for so long.... I see a light...Someone's coming...I'm dragged into a rowboat...I'm saved...."

In another session, Chaim went back to a childhood incident. "I'm scared all the time; there's so much fighting and shooting going on. The Arabs are trying to kill us."

"How old are you?" Stephen asked

"Six years old."

"What year is it?"

"1947."

"What's happening?"

"My mother just went out to collect the eggs. I'm home alone...There's a gigantic boom...The walls are shaking...I'm running from room to room...looking for my mother...No one is here...I'm scared...I'm screaming...crying...the Arabs are coming...No one is here to watch over me...What if the Arabs come?...I get some stones and rocks from the garden to throw at bad people...Someone is coming...I throw the stones at her...It's my mother...I thought she was an Arab coming to take me away...."

After the session, Chaim filled Stephen in on the historical facts of that episode. His mother had explained to him what had happened once she herself found out.

In November of 1947, shortly before the Israel War of Independence, the ongoing tensions erupted into civil war between the Arab and Jewish populations. At that time, Afula was served by the Jezreel Valley Railway. Exactly when Chaim's mother had gone to collect the eggs, the Jewish underground militias blew up the railway lines connecting Afula to Jenin. The explosion was powerful enough to cause the walls of their house to shake.

The third incident took Chaim even further back in time. It occurred when he was a baby. Of course, he had no conscious recollection of it but he knew what had happened as a story told to him by his mother. And under hypnosis he gave a very clear account of exactly what had happened.

"I'm sitting in the carriage in the front yard. I'm strapped in but have some leeway to twist from side to side as I look around...A dog just walked into the yard...he's barking so hard...I'm scared...He keeps on barking...I try to back away from him...I lean over the edge of the carriage...Ooooh...I'm falling...I'm upside down...hanging by the carriage straps...I'm screaming hysterically, kicking and kicking, but the dog won't stop barking...Where's Mommy?...I'm screaming...She comes...."

Stephen explained to us that this may have been the initial sensitizing event, the first of all the similar events that started off the process of his terror response.

There may have been other triggering incidents in Chaim's life, however, it was not necessary to uncover all of them. Stephen said that as long as he dealt with the ones that Chaim's subconscious mind had brought to the surface during therapy, he could successfully neutralize the old pattern of terror and create a new, healthy pattern in the present, one that would be activated whenever Chaim was subjected to the triggers of loud and frightening noises. Time would show us whether he had accomplished the goal or not.

"Why did my terror attacks appear only after the hiking accident and not after those other incidents that occurred earlier in my life?" Chaim wanted to know.

"Apparently," Stephen said, "each incident in and of itself was not powerful enough to create your terror attacks in response to loud noises. However, after the initial sensitizing episode, each subsequent incident reinforced the need to scream, flail, and throw things. Then, after numerous incidents, there came the accident that acted as the 'straw that broke the camel's back.' Your feelings of helplessness, accompanied by the loud noises of the rescue helicopter, associated you with all of those old incidents stored in your memory in which screaming, flailing, and throwing had seemed to be the best response.

"Your brain had learned that loud noises always came with a situation of helplessness, and therefore it was necessary to respond in the way that had helped you in the past. This response had become embedded in your psyche and it felt as though you had no control over it. However, through hypnotherapy your psyche has learned, and is still in the process of learning, a new and better response. There is nothing that you have to do consciously since your subconscious will automatically bring the 'adult' Chaim to calm the 'child' Chaim whenever the irrational emotions are triggered."

At one of our visits Stephen brought up the issue of the anxiety medications.

"Chaim, I'd like you to wean yourself off the antianxiety pills in order for us to see how well you are actually doing. If, after being drug-free for a reasonable amount of time, you no longer respond with terror attacks to the old triggers, then we will know you are healed."

"Sure. That makes sense." I think Chaim was looking forward to getting off the drugs, to knowing that it was in his power to calm himself rather than being dependent on the medications.

In light of the fact that Chaim felt comfortable and productive in London, it was relatively easy for him to wean himself off the antianxiety medication. It took him over two months, but once he was off the pills he realized that he really had no need for them. During that time, Chaim found the old panicky feelings stirring within only on a few occasions, but they were easily overcome and banished.

One evening Chaim and I were sitting in the dining room. He was preparing his *shiurim* and I was knitting. The house was cozy, although a violent thunderstorm was raging outside. I noticed that Chaim would look up from his *sefarim* from time to time; he was clearly distracted by the crashing peals of thunder and the shrieking of the wind. Suddenly, we were thrown into a déjà vu experience, as the wailing of a siren grew louder and louder when an ambulance rushed by. Chaim stiffened for a moment and then looked at me and smiled. I smiled back. Tears blurred my vision as I realized that after all these long months of struggle, he was finally free.

WE DECIDE TO STAY

It seemed too good to be true, and we wanted to be completely sure that the attacks were, indeed, gone. Stephen put Chaim through simulated noise tests, and after several trials it was quite apparent that Chaim could be present in the middle of an air raid with sirens blaring and he would respond as any other person would. Thank Hashem, Chaim Simcha Perlman was healed!

Although essentially we were now free to go home because our goal had been accomplished, we decided we would not do so right then. Chaim felt close to his students and wanted to see them finish the school year. He was also helping them prepare for *yeshiva gedolah* entrance exams and was interested in seeing which student was accepted to which yeshiva. Some of them were planning to continue their learning in Eretz Yisrael and he was investing extra effort in helping them get accepted. He had no desire to leave them before the end of the year.

Chaim had also started putting in hours for Journeys and he greatly enjoyed his work in *kiruv*. Working with people one-on-one really gave him satisfaction. He had a way with them and his bosses were pleased with his accomplishments. The organization was planning a large-scale weekend retreat during the summer school break and he had been given quite a responsible job in planning the affair. He was keen on being a part of it.

We had invited Joe to join us for Pesach and we were thrilled when he accepted our invitation. Unbeknown to him, I had my eye on a young lady that I'd met at the school bazaar. She worked as a secretary for Yesodey Hatorah and I was impressed with her refined manner. She reminded me of a fragrant English rose.

When I made inquiries, I found out that she was a *baalas teshuvah* for quite a number of years, and lived in a rented flat with several other girls. I invited her on several occasions for a Shabbos meal and each time she came, my liking for her grew. So I too was keen on staying in London, at least until after Joe's visit to our home.

Leaving London after Pesach was not a very practical option either, as the baby was due a month later. We figured that we might as well give the privilege of British citizenship to at least one of our children. Who could know how that might benefit him one day in the future?

Additionally, I had a dream of becoming certified in hypnosis. I was aware that Stephen was giving a course in the summer break. Participating meant I'd have to study a fair amount of written modules on my own and then take the three-week hands-on training in a group setting. Chaim was as keen as I was about my doing the course. We both felt that as a *frum* practicing hypnotist I could help women in ways previously unavailable to them.

Rav Scheinerman agreed to my taking the course on the condition that I would always sit next to and practice exercises with a woman student. Certain that I could fulfill those conditions, I immediately asked Mother if she could arrange her summer visit to us to coincide with the dates of the course. She readily agreed, understanding my deep desire to certify in hypnosis. With Mother as the perfect babysitter, I felt that now my dream could indeed become reality.

WE MOVE

As excited as Chaim and I were with our upcoming plans, the most pressing thing on my mind was getting ready for Pesach, only a few weeks off. Physical work at this time was difficult for me, to say the least. Just caring for the four children and putting in a few hours of work weekly with teaching and photography took up all my time and energy. The house was old and hard to clean, and, worst of all, chilly. I had put up with the inconveniences till now because we had not really thought of staying in London all that long. But now that we were thinking of extending our sojourn in this country I broached the idea to Chaim of looking for a more comfortable flat. Moving into a modern apartment would make my Pesach cleaning immeasurably easier.

Chaim was not interested in paying a higher rent, as we could barely afford the rent we were currently paying. But late one night, as I straightened up after teaching, I heard some strange noises in the kitchen. I went to see what it was and to my utter dismay I saw a long thin tail disappearing behind the refrigerator! I stifled a scream, and ran into the bedroom.

"Chaim! Chaim! Wake up! We are definitely moving! I won't stay here another day!! I just saw the tail end of a mouse in the kitchen!"

"Take it easy, Sari," he tried calming me down as he rubbed the sleep from his eyes. "Don't worry! We're not the first person in London to have to deal with this. I'm sure that a sturdy mouse trap will put an end to the difficulty."

Or so he thought! To be on the safe side, we invested in a dozen of them.

Every time I heard a trap snap shut, mostly when trying to fall asleep at night, I was completely shaken up. Despite our best efforts, we could not vanquish the seemingly endless supply of British rodents! So after a week of struggle we decided to bring in an exterminator.

He warned us not to let children or pets near the poison he was putting behind the fridge and the stove and in the basement. I prayed to Hashem that the children would be safe and was sure that the problem would be solved.

One morning when I went to wake the little ones up for school I found out otherwise. I was standing at the edge of Miri's bed, transfixed by what I saw.

"Miri! Miri!" My voice was loud enough to awaken, but not so loud as to frighten her. "Come here, to Mommy! Come on," I coaxed, "come to Mommy!" The moment she was in arm's reach I picked her up. There, in the bed, was a dead mouse.

That was the straw that broke the camel's back.

"Chaim, we have to move! I just can't take it anymore!" I was on the verge of hysterics.

"OK! OK! We'll go to the real estate agent after work."

"All the old houses are infested with mice," the agent explained to us. "Since the buildings are attached, the mice manage to bore their way from one house to another, and poison has to be put down repeatedly. That's why so many families own cats."

"I don't want to have a cat in the house!" I told him. "I think I'm allergic to them."

"Well, if you won't have a cat living in, you'll have to move into a relatively newly built housing complex. How much rent are you willing to spend?"

We gave him our price range.

"The ones that are more cheaply priced border on Stamford Hill. If you don't mind living a few minutes' walk outside of Stamford Hill proper I have several flats to show you."

"I'd like you to show us the flats that are available for immediate occupancy," Chaim said.

"Sure." The agent spent a few moments searching through his files. "I've got two that are available right away. One of them is fully furnished and the rent is quite high, out of the price range you mentioned. The other is equipped with electrical appliances and no furniture, but the rent fits your pocket. It's also freshly painted. You could furnish the flat by applying to the Ezer v'Chessed organization. They own a tremendous warehouse stocked with used furniture and electrical appliances that they sell for next to nothing."

We decided to go with the unfurnished flat since the rent was reasonable and it was located a seven-minute walk from Chaim's yeshiva. In a matter of two days we managed to buy most of the furniture we needed. And so, two weeks later we moved into our new flat. With the help of our dear brother and sister-in-law and friends we managed doing so without too much of a hassle. At least I saved on cleaning closets, as I arranged the freshly laundered clothes into the freshly painted closets.

I was thrilled to be living in a house with central heating and plenty of hot water for baths and showers. Another plus was the large dining room facing a sunny backyard. It suited our needs perfectly, for ever since Chaim had started working with Journeys we always had Shabbos guests.

Besides the three upstairs bedrooms, there was a small study on the first floor. I decided to share that room with Chaim as my photography studio. Chaim's *sefarim* would prominently occupy one wall and my scenic backdrops would adorn the other ones. We prepared our guest room lovingly, knowing that soon Joe would be with us.

GETTING READY FOR PESACH

Pesach was around the corner and there was a lot to do to get ready. Chaim had to buy counter covers and Pesach sinks for the kitchen and I had to do the food shopping and get the kitchen ready for cooking and baking. Having no car meant we were at the mercy of the shop owners to deliver our goods in a reasonable amount of time (which wasn't always the case).

We were feeling quite overwhelmed with all that had to be done, when Joe called asking if he could come on Rosh Chodesh Nissan, the beginning of *bein hazemanim*. Gratefully, we assured him it would be our greatest pleasure. Having another pair of hands around to do things and another pair of legs to run errands for two whole weeks was the best thing that could have happened to us right then. It was a custom-tailored plan from Heaven!

Ari invited us for the two *sedarim*, but the walk from our new home to theirs was more than the children could manage. The Stefanskys invited us for the *sedarim* as well. Their house was within walking distance for the children and we decided to have the first Seder at home and the second Seder with our good friends.

Now, all I had to do was get my act together and get my work done as efficiently as I could. This was easier said than done. When I stood without walking around for more than a few minutes, my blood pressure dropped and I felt faint. I simply had to learn to do my work sitting down. Malky sent me one or the other of her girls to help out, but I sent her home as quickly as I could. I knew that if I completely refused to have them over Malky would be hurt. Her greatest pleasure was in doing good deeds for others. But she was due several months after I was and I knew she needed their help as much or more than I did.

I preferred to pay for my help. I thought of Janet, the school secretary, the one I had my eye on for Joe. If she could help me get the kitchen ready for cooking, and then do the peeling, chopping, and washing up, what could be better? That was surely more important to me than having someone wash windows. Yes, Janet was definitely a good idea!

She liked my offer, as extra cash was always needed when one was self-supporting. I arranged for her to come to work for two hours daily. It would appear quite natural for us to suggest the *shidduch* to Joe when the time was right.

JOE ARRIVES

Joe arrived as planned, the evening of Rosh Chodesh Nissan. With great fanfare, he breezed into our house, bringing gifts for the children and letters from friends and students, accompanied by a big bunch of flowers. Of course, I had a freshly baked chocolate cake ready for him (baked in Malky's oven, as she had both a chametz and a Pesach kitchen). Right on cue, Joe quipped, "Thanks, Mrs. Perlman. Nothing beats homemade chocolate cake!" The children could not understand why Chaim, Joe, and I all burst out laughing.

It was a touch of home, our real home, Joe brought with him. We sat for hours talking about everyone and everything going on in Eretz Yisrael, despite the fact that it was Erev Pesach. It was a break well worth taking.

"You must be tired, Joe," I finally said, when I noticed how late it was. "It's time to call it a night."

"Yes and no, Mrs. Perlman. The trip was tiring but seeing you both and the sweet kids really invigorated me," he replied. "I guess I should go to sleep, though, if I'm going to be of any help to you tomorrow."

"You sleep as long as you want," Chaim said. "You didn't come here to help us, just to be our guest. I'll wake you before the *zeman* and after you daven you can go back to sleep."

"Don't worry, Reb Chaim. I'll catch up on my sleep when Pesach comes in. I want you to remember Yosef Levine as the *bochur* who made your life easier and more pleasurable. I want you to *shep nachas* from all the sweat that you invested in me!"

I was very touched. Was I imagining it or were Chaim's eyes wet? He cleared his throat before speaking.

"Joe, you're a great guy! You'll go a long way in life! So now you call yourself Yosef? Is that what you want us to call you?"

"Whatever feels good to you, Reb Chaim. My old friends still call me Joe, but I am trying to switch over to Yosef. It's better for the *shidduch* scene."

I sneaked a look at Chaim and he winked at me. I planned on serving lunch the next day at one-thirty and Janet was due to arrive at 1:45. Inevitably, they would see each other. After an appropriate amount of time Chaim would speak to Joe about Janet and I would speak to her about Joe. But at this point all I could think about was the bed that was beckoning me to come.

PESACH

The calendar waits for no one, including the Perlman family, and the 15th of Nissan arrived exactly when it was meant to come, whether I was ready for it or not. But this year I was ready. With Joe's, Janet's, and the Stefansky girls' help I was actually better off than in previous years. The Pesach Seder was an amazing experience, both in our home and at the Stefanskys. All the aches and pains and exhaustion evaporated when I was finally sitting at the Seder table, the matriarch of my family. I guided the children in following along with the Haggadah. I had coached them in learning the *Mah Nishtanah* and they did a great job.

After the pre-Pesach exertions, I needed to be off my feet. Joe and Chaim took over serving the meals and clearing the table. I truly felt like a queen. Slowly my batteries were refilling, in time for me to give birth.

On Chol Hamoed we went on several outings, some with Ari and his family. It was great fun. The weather was mild and the gardens were blooming. There was freshness in the air. No one wanted the *chag* to end.

I was pleased when Joe finally asked us about Janet. He wanted to know her background and where she was from. "She's a very refined young woman with sterling character traits; I think she'd be really good for you, Joe. Would you like me to speak to her about going out with you?"

"Yeah, I think I'd like to give it a try. Could you do that for me, Mrs. Perlman?"

"Sure, Joe. I'll speak to her tonight." It didn't take much persuasion on my part to get Janet to agree to meet our Israeli guest.

On their first date, Janet gave Joe a tour of London Town and they hit it off well. His plan was to return to Eretz Yisrael by Rosh Chodesh Iyar to start the new learning *zeman* on schedule. Now he had to make a decision. Should he follow his original plan or should he continue seeing Janet and delay his return to Eretz Yisrael? Janet was interested in Joe, but obviously, she could not tell him to stay.

"I really don't know what to do, Reb Chaim," Joe expressed his dilemma one day. "If I stay and it doesn't work out and I come back late to yeshiva, I'll have a really hard time catching up and...."

"Listen, Joe, don't feel pressured," Chaim tried to calm Joe down. "You certainly don't have to rush things. If you need more time, you can return to Eretz Yisrael to figure things out from there. After all, the distance from Eretz Yisrael to London is not that great. And, remember, you're always welcome as our guest whenever you feel like it." Joe was still unclear as to what to do.

Janet's parents had been killed in a car accident when she was sixteen years old. It was that accident that acted as a catalyst in her becoming religious. Luckily for Janet, she had an old great-aunt, Feiga Schorr, on her mother's side, living in Liverpool. She was a descendant of the Kishinever dynasty and very religious. She was completely lucid and was able to tell Janet exactly who all her forbears were.

On one of their dates, Janet took Joe to visit her. Tante Feiga had bundles of photos of Janet's great-grandparents, grandparents, her mother as a child, and her aunts, uncles, and cousins. She was a treasure house of information, familiar with every branch of Janet's family tree. And she even knew that her niece had been named Chaya at birth. Joe was impressed with the fact that Janet actually stemmed from an aristocratic Rumanian family.

"Children," Tante Feiga hugged Janet as they were about to leave. "May you have a long and fruitful life together! Chaya and Yosef, I see that you are perfectly suited to each other! May your parents in Heaven have much *yiddishe nachas* from both of you!"

She couldn't understand, despite their telling her repeatedly, that they were not engaged. Her blessings embraced them as they made the trip back to London. Joe was thoughtful but still remained uncommitted. He had no idea why it was so hard for him to decide.

A PREMATURE HAPPENING

As the day of departure drew close, Joe started slowly packing his bags. He wanted to see how a separation would affect him and whether there would be more clarity of mind in the Holy Land.

However, "Man plans and G-d laughs." Two nights before he was scheduled to leave, I went into premature labor, twenty-five days early. The next day I gave birth to a nearly four-pound baby boy. He was tiny, but healthy. Since I would spend most of my time in the hospital until the baby was big enough to be discharged and Chaim was scheduled to begin teaching imminently, Joe made the decision to remain in London to help us through our predicament.

Joe decided to learn in a local *yeshiva gedolah* in addition to a learning *chavrusa* with Chaim. In his spare time, he offered to shop and cook for us. Chaim planned on learning with Joe in the *beis medrash* down the road. During the time they were out of the house, Janet would straighten up, do the laundry, and bathe the children before I would come home in the evenings to put them to bed with a goodnight story.

Chaim's schedule was intense, teaching in the mornings, preparing his lessons for the next day, learning with Joe, and then alternating with me at the hospital. We wanted to spend as much of our time with our newborn as possible. We had no idea how long it would take the baby to gain the two pounds or so that he needed in order to be discharged. I was encouraged to touch him by inserting my hands into the incubator, and even gently massage him. My pumped milk was fed to him through a nose tube. At some point I would be allowed to feed him by bottle and then, as he gained strength, eventually begin nursing him. Since it was vital for me to be with my new baby as much as I possibly could, without Joe's constant presence and help I didn't know how we would have managed.

By the time "baby" was out of the hospital and his *bris milah* performed, Joe and Janet were engaged. Janet had been such an outstanding, loving, and caring surrogate mother to the children that he came to appreciate her in an entirely new way. He no longer had any doubts that she was his *zivug hagun*. As we counted grams on the baby scale, Yosef and Janet, who now called herself Chaya, counted the days to their marriage. We were blessed with a very happy double simchah to celebrate and thank Hashem for.

I was struck by the wisdom of the precept to always look for the silver lining in every cloud. I clearly could see the "good" that had come out of my unfortunate premature birth. It had been the reason for Joe staying on in London and getting to know Janet better. Had he gone back to Eretz Yisrael, who knows if he would have returned? And so, Hashem kept him in London until he realized that his *bashert* was right there waiting for him to realize the fact.

At the *bris milah* they announced their engagement, to everyone's great joy. We called the baby Avrohom Yeshayahu, after the Chazon Ish.[18] I hoped he would always usher in good news, as did the *navi* Yeshayahu in his famous words, "*Nachamu, nachamu ami* — be comforted, be comforted my nation."[19]

CHAPTER TEN

Goals Achieved

THE WEDDING

Yosef and Chaya decided to live in B'nei Brak, but the wedding would take place in London. Yosef's parents planned on coming from the United States with his two siblings. How excited we were to hear that Rabbi Reichman and some of Yosef's closest friends had decided to come from Eretz Yisrael to take part in his simchah. Oh, how I wished that Bina would join them; how I longed to see her! Of course, it was just a dream. I knew that the Reichmans didn't have the means to spend in that way.

Bina Reichman had assured the young couple that she'd unpack the suitcases with household goods they sent ahead of their arrival into the furnished apartment she'd found for them. The wedding was set for the month of Tamuz and after Tishah b'Av, they would leave for B'nei Brak. I would miss them sorely.

The wedding was a stunning affair, generously paid for by Yosef's parents. Chaya was an absolute queen, a glowing beauty. She arranged for Tante Feiga to be brought over in a wheelchair with her caretaker in attendance. The old lady's blessing had come to fruition, and Chaya felt as though her mother's spirit was being represented by her elderly aunt at the wedding.

When the time came for the newlyweds to leave, I arranged a goodbye party in our home. It was a mixture of tasty food, gifts, laughter, and tears; happiness on the one hand for the good fortune of the young couple, and sadness at seeing them go. I took lots of photos and placed them in an album. This was the beginning of my "*Kallah* Album." It served as a record of the many matches I would merit to make in my lifetime. (Of course, Mike and Bassy's pictures found their way into it as well, as soon as I was able to dig them out of their original album.) It was testimony to the fact that one act of *chessed* could literally affect generations of people and give a person countless merit.

BABY AVRUMI

I found that my time was nearly completely taken up with caring for Avrumi and the rest of the family. He ate around the clock, and I was pleased that he had such a lusty appetite. He still had some catching up to do with his weight, but was closing the gap rather quickly. Although I was busy feeding him very often, I was blessed, indeed, with a content and placid baby in between feeds. During those breaks I studied Stephen's written modules in preparation for the hypnotherapy training. By the time the course started, I'd make sure to get Avrumi used to drinking milk from a bottle.

MOTHER ARRIVES

The day of my mother's arrival finally came. We hired a van to the airport, as all the Perlmans were going to meet her. I dressed them in their Shabbos finery as I wanted my mother to see how precious her visit was to us. It was no mean feat getting the five of them dressed and spruced up on time, but where there is a will there is a way.

When I need a happy memory to lift my spirits, I recall the scene of Mother's meeting with the children at Heathrow airport. Excitement and joyful energy throbbed all around and engulfed us. The sounds reverberate in my mind till today.

"Bubby! Bubby!" the childish voices rang out, accompanied by their waving arms. "Here, Bubby, here we are!"

And then, one gigantic embrace, with laughter and tears cascading around us all at once! Avrumi, caught in the crush and the noisy embrace, began crying. Mother took him in her arms, cooing and rocking him gently. Within seconds he was calm and cooing back at her as though they were the best of friends. I knew my little one would be safe and happy in those loving arms while I was away doing my course.

CERTIFICATION

Mother was an angel in disguise. I couldn't imagine having been able to survive the intensity of the three-week hypnosis course had she not been there. My gratitude knew no bounds as I walked through the door on the last day of the course with my certificate in hand.

"You're glowing!" Chaim said. He took my packages from me as I plopped down into our single armchair. He then sat down next to me. "So, how was it, Dr. Perlman?"

"Oh, stop joking!" I laughed. "I'm still plain little Sari Perlman, with an extra skill or two for helping people. I bet they would be useful in *kiruv* work too. You want to learn some of it?"

"No, thanks. My scholarship lies in different areas. But I can send you my tough nuts when I fail to crack them myself." It was good to see Chaim calm and relaxed and in such a good mood. Hypnosis had been a lifesaver for us and I was proud to have actually become certified. I could now help others as we'd been helped.

Mother entered the room with Avrumi in her arms.

"I thought I heard your voice, Sari." She came over and passed me the baby. I snuggled him lovingly and then gave her a hug and a kiss.

"How can I even begin to thank you, Mother, for all you did for us? You must be exhausted! I wish you could stay a little longer and relax before you go home."

"I'd love to stay on but I can't delay my return home," Mother said. "Father is waiting impatiently for me."

"I know," I said. "It's so good of him to let you come. I hope I can travel to the US to see him with Avrumi sometime soon."

"Maybe we'll plan a trip with the whole family to see you and Dad," Chaim said.

"Oh, that would be great!" Mother exclaimed.

I wasn't expecting to hear that from Chaim; he wasn't the sentimental type. As far as I knew, we owed money on the moving expenses, and his salary did not allow us to put away savings. Without my parents' help we could never have managed the finances. Maybe he had just said it to be nice. I was too enveloped with sadness at Mother's leaving to come up with any other explanation.

"Let's have supper," I said. "Right now, that's all I can think about."

Mother went to the kitchen to warm up the food while I trekked upstairs to the children's room. My angels were in bed, waiting for me. We had our goodnight story, cuddles, and kisses, and a promise to go to the park the next day.

I enjoyed a leisurely supper with Chaim and Mother, as we planned our park outing and a boat ride. I contemplated the pleasure of just enjoying ourselves in nature, without any pressure or need to perform. Just to be! After my exertions over the last couple of years, that would be utter luxury!

Mother's visit was wonderful, but all good things come to an end, as they say.

"Sari," my Mother said, as we sat alone together the night before she left, "I can't tell you how proud I am of you. Few women could have handled what you handled. You didn't give up until your husband was cured. You didn't fall into depression. You didn't let your marriage fall apart. You didn't let your kids get hurt. You moved to a new land and kept your family strong and beautiful. And now you've become a certified hypnotist in order to help others! You're quite a woman. I couldn't be prouder."

Her words touched me to the core. As I embraced her, I had no thoughts or worries about my future as a hypnotherapist.

A NEW BEGINNING

My first client came from a most unexpected source. When I excitedly told Malky about receiving my certification in hypnosis, she became quite serious.

She hesitated for a moment and then said, "Sari, do you think you could undo old trauma?"

I was taken aback for a moment by her words. I wondered what skeleton was hiding in her closet. I turned to her with a soft smile and said, "That depends on the situation. Would you like to tell me more about it?"

"I'm talking about myself, Sari." She was having a hard time getting the words out, but she bravely continued. "As calm as I seem, I do have a morbid fear of giving birth."

It seemed that Malky had suffered severely in the past, once due to the birth of a brain-damaged child whom she'd had to institutionalize and, several years later, due to a stillbirth. I was totally unaware of these two episodes in her life. As a result of her trauma, each pregnancy and birth that followed caused her untold anxiety and debilitating panic attacks. She was asking me if I could disassociate the present from what had happened to her in the past.

As daunting as the task appeared, I accepted it. Hashem was presenting me with my first hypnotherapy challenge and it wasn't an easy one.

Stephen kindly helped me formulate a treatment plan. Malky and I had three very productive sessions and I scheduled a fourth. But it never took place.

I got the call from the hospital a day before our scheduled meeting. How diametrically opposite it was to the one I had received from a Jerusalem hospital almost three years earlier to the day, the call that had shattered my life and the lives of my family.

"Sari! It's me, Malky. I'm calling from the 'City of London'!"

"Malky! Did you give birth? Are you OK?!"

"*Chasdei Hashem*! I had a baby girl last night!"

"Malky, are you serious? Mazel tov! Mazel tov!! Is everything OK?"

"Sari, it's unbelievable! It was amazing! Even though I was taken by surprise when I went into labor and worried that I wasn't completely prepared, you won't believe it, I remained calm the whole time. I just can't fathom that I actually had a wonderful experience."

"Malky, I'm so happy for you! It really does sound too good to be true. But tell me more about how you managed."

"It was just like you said to me in trance, that I would be able to maintain control over my feelings by using my breathing and relaxation techniques. And I was able to do that for the many hours of labor. Sari, I have to say — my birth experience was a great success!"

When I came to visit her in the hospital, she hugged me tightly and burst out crying. I shed a few tears myself, tears of happiness.

"Sari, I'm so happy! I can't understand how just a few hours of hypnosis could release years of fear and panic."

"I'll tell you the truth, Malky, it's hard for me to comprehend it too. But that's the nature of hypnosis and the power of the subconscious mind."

"I'm eternally grateful to you, Sari! Come, let's go see the baby."

In the nursery, Malky placed her beautiful, healthy infant in my arms. The baby's tiny fingers curled around my pinky finger, as though to acknowledge the part I had played in her special debut into the world.

I felt myself flying! I was on cloud nine! I had actually helped a dear friend with a serious problem through hypnotherapy. How many times had I been incapable of opening my mouth to say the words I needed to say? Now, by the grace of Hashem, I was a different person. The Almighty had blessed me with the ability to turn speech into my friend, my strength, my ally.

I could barely believe it!

It had all been worth it, this seemingly crazy idea of moving to England. First and foremost, there was Chaim's healing. Our lives had been transformed by that. Any effort was worth our achieving that outcome. And now it became as clear as day that it had been worth all the money we had invested in my education, the studying for months in advance, and the intense effort of those three weeks of training.

The feeling of flying stayed with me for hours. I was on a different plane, a state of revelation.

Enlightenment!

Was it possible to gain even more enlightenment? I could not know, as the future was hidden from me. But one thing I did know was that I'd discovered an amazing facet of my purpose for being in this world.

My mind reverted to a time when I had felt totally insecure, when endless happenings had intimidated me beyond comprehension to a point of being frozen in helplessness.

The inability to escape the confines of my limitations had entrapped me in a deep, dark, seemingly bottomless pit. Enveloped in darkness, I couldn't see my way out, the way to break free. I couldn't even imagine that there was a "light at the end of the tunnel."

I could not see the way out, but Hashem could. Only He could devise a plan for me to become who I was meant to be. As the darkest moments of night give way to the rays of daybreak, my transformation as well took me from darkness to dawn.

Hashem had allowed me to be filled with the light of a new day, a new beginning. With His continued support, I would discover even greater vistas of light.

ENDNOTES

1   This fictionalized doctor was inspired by Dr. David Applebaum, *Hy"d*, an American physician and a trauma care specialist and neurologist in Sha'arei Tzedek Hospital, who was killed in a terrorist attack at Café Hillel with his daughter Nava the day before her wedding.

2   Psalms 51:17.

3   Exodus 14:13.

4   Ibid. 14:15.

5   *Ethics of the Fathers*, concluding paragraph of each chapter. Translation in Artscroll PA.

6   Words often said by the sage Rabbi Akiva, as found in the story in *Berachos* 60b.

7   A paraphrase of the words of a part of the classic Amidah: *Baruch atah Hashem rofei cholei amo Yisrael* — Blessed are You Hashem who heals the sick of His nation Yisrael.

8   Deuteronomy 4:35.

9   Chassidic maxim.

10   Psalms 100:2.

11   Deuteronomy 16:14.

12   Psalms 121:4.

13   Rashi in *Parashas Balak*, Numbers 22:35, from *Bamidbar Rabbah*.

14   Modeled after Roy Hunter, professional hypnotherapist in Washington State, USA.

15   Modeled after Stephen Brooks, professional hypnotherapist in Thailand and Great Britain, founder of British Hypnosis Research and Training Institute.

16   *Ethics of the Fathers* 5:26.17

17   *Pesikta Zutreta, Esther* 4:17.

18   Rabbi Avrohom Yeshaya Karelitz, popularly known by the name of his major Torah work, entitled *Chazon Ish*. From Kosava, Russia he became one of the leaders of *chareidi* (ultra-Orthodox) Jewry in Eretz Yisrael, where his final twenty years, 1933–1953, were spent.

19   Isaiah 40:1.

GLOSSARY

Abba	Father.
aleph-beis	The Hebrew alphabet; the Hebrew letters for A and B.
aliyah	Moving to Israel from the Diaspora.
Am Yisrael	The nation of Israel.
avodas Hashem	Service of G-d.
baal teshuvah	Male returnee to Judaism.
baalas teshuvah	Female returnee to Judaism.
baalei teshuvah	Returnees to Judaism.
bar mitzvah	A thirteen-year-old Jewish boy. The day he turns thirteen, he takes on the yoke of mitzvah observance.
baruch Hashem	Blessed be G-d.
Baruch Rofei cholim	Blessed is the Healer of the ill, i.e., G-d.
bashert	Heavenly designated mate.
b'derech she'adam rotzeh leileich bah molichin oso	
	The way one desires to go, so will he be led.
b'ezras Hashem	With Hashem's help.
bein hazemanim	The yeshiva intercession, three to four weeks in duration three times a year

219

Beis Hamikdash	The Holy Temple.
beis medrash	Study hall of the yeshiva or synagogue.
ben	Son of.
berachah	Ritual blessing over food or drink or said when doing a commandment. *Also,* a blessing for good to be bestowed upon the listener.
Beruchim Haba'im	Welcome.
Bikur Cholim Society	Society for visiting and aiding the sick.
bimheirah	quickly.
bitachon	Trust (in G-d).
Bituach Leumi	Israel National Insurance Institute.
bli ayin hara	Without an evil eye. This is said in an effort to avert an "evil eye" or bad luck from oneself or others.
B'nei Yisrael	The Nation of Israel.
bochur	Single male; male youth.
bris milah	Circumcision.
b'siyata d'Shmaya	With Heavenly assistance.
Bubby	(Yiddish) Grandmother.
chaburah	A Talmudic study group for men or older boys.
chag	Holiday.
chagim	Holidays.
challah	Traditional Shabbos bread, braided or formed into other shapes.
chametz	Leavening, forbidden on the Passover holiday.
chareidi	Ultra-Orthodox Jewry.
chas v'shalom	G-d forbid.
chasadim	Plural of *chessed*, loving-kindnesses.

chasdei Hashem	(Acts of) loving-kindness of G-d.
Chassidic	Following in the ways of the Chassidic Rebbe of one's choosing.
chavrusa	Study partner.
Chazal	An acronym for *chachmeinu zichronam livrachah* — our Sages of blessed memory.
chazan	Cantor for Jewish prayers.
cheder	The traditional grade school for religious Jewish boys.
chessed	An act of loving-kindness.
Chol Hamoed	The intermediary days of the holidays of Passover and Sukkos.
Chumash	Pentateuch; one of the Five Books of Moses.
chuppah	The wedding canopy, under which the religious part of the marriage ceremony takes place.
chutz la'aretz	Outside of the Land; any country other than Israel.
daas Torah	Torah viewpoint or truth articulated by a Torah scholar.
dan l'chaf zechus	Giving the benefit of the doubt; judging favorably.
daven	Pray.
davened	Past tense of pray.
davening	Praying.
Dodah	Aunt in Hebrew.
Dovid Hamelech	King David, composer of Psalms.
dreidel	Small spinning toy played with on Chanukah.
d'var Torah	A Torah discourse or speech.
Elul	The sixth month of the Jewish calendar; the month before Rosh Hashanah.
emunah	Faith.
Eretz Yisrael	The land of Israel.

Erev Pesach	The day of the eve of Passover; the days prior to Passover.
Ezer v'Chessed	Lit., help and kindness; the name of an organization.
frum	Religious, mitzvah observant.
gan	Kindergarten.
gan chovah	Compulsory preschool kindergarten comparable to pre-1A.
Gemara	Talmud.
Haggadah	The Jewish text that delineates the Passover Seder, the ritual conducted on Passover night.
Hakadosh Baruch Hu	The Holy One, blessed be He.
halachah	Jewish law.
halachic	Relating to halachah.
Hashem	G-d.
Hashem Hu haElokim, ein od milvado	Hashem is the Almighty, there is no one but Him.
hashgachah pratis	Divine intervention.
Hishtadlus	Effort.
Hy"d	An acronym for *Hashem yikom damo*; lit., "May Hashem avenge his blood," an expression used when speaking about a Jewish martyr.
im yirtzeh Hashem	G-d willing.
Ima	Mother in Hebrew.
Ivdu es Hashem b'simchah	Serve Hashem with joy.
Iyar	The second month of the Jewish calendar; the month following Passover.
kallah	Bride.

kehillah	Community.
Keitzad Merakdim	"How do we dance [before the bride]?"; the name of a Jewish song.
kippah	Skullcap.
kiruv	Bringing estranged Jews close/closer to their roots.
Kitzur Shulchan Aruch	
	A summary of the *Shulchan Aruch*, the Jewish code of law.
kodesh	Holy or religious.
Kol mahn d'avid Rachmana l'tav avid	
	Aramaic for "All that the Merciful One does, He does for good."
kollel	Torah institute of learning for married men, which supports them with a monetary stipend.
kriyas Yam Suf	The splitting of the Red (Reed) Sea, occurring after the exodus of the Jewish nation from Egypt.
kugel	Traditional baked Jewish dish, made from potatoes, other vegetables, or leftover bread.
kupat cholim	Israeli health care provider.
lashon hakodesh	The holy tongue; Hebrew.
lashon hara	Evil speech; speaking derogatorily about others.
Lev L'Achim	Israeli organization, roughly translated as "heart to brothers," which aims to spread Torah to all Jewish people.
L'fum tzarah agra	The reward is in proportion to the exertion.
Maariv	The evening prayer.
Maasei chessed	Acts of loving-kindness.
Mah Nishtanah	One of the sections of the Passover Haggadah,

where the children ask questions of the father about the rituals of the night.

malachim	Angels.
mazel tov	Congratulations.
mechitzah	A partition separating the men's and women's sections in the synagogue, at a wedding, or party.
mehadrin kosher	A most stringent level of kosher.
melamdim	Teachers.
mesiras nefesh	Lit., "giving over one's life"; self-sacrifice; dedication.
metukah	Sweetie.
middas hadin	The attribute of justice.
Minchah	The afternoon prayer.
minyan	Quorum of Jewish males over the age of thirteen needed for praying and other religious activities.
Mishnah	The first written compilation of the Oral Torah, redacted by Rabbi Yehudah Hanasi. It is the precursor to the Talmud, and contains six orders.
Mishnayos	Plural of Mishnah.
Mishnayos Shabbos	A section of the codified Oral Law, titled "Shabbos."
Mitzrayim	Egypt.
mitzvah	Torah commandment.
mitzvos	Torah commandments.
Modeh ani	"I gratefully thank You"; the first prayer upon opening one's eyes in the morning.
Morah	Female teacher.
Moshe Rabbeinu	Moses our teacher.
Motzaei Shabbos	The nighttime after the holiness of the Sabbath has departed.

Mussaf	The second prayer said on the Sabbath and holidays.
Nachamu, nachamu ami	
	"Be comforted, be comforted my nation."
nachas; nachas ruach	
	Gratification and pleasure a parent has from their child, or G-d from His children. *See "shep nachas."*
navi	Prophet.
negel vasser	The ritual washing of one's hands upon awakening from sleep in the morning. It is an act of sanctification of one's hands for performing G-d's service in life.
Negev	Southern part of Israel, mostly desert.
Ne'ilah	Lit., locking; the fifth and last prayer of Yom Kippur, which refers to the locking of the Gates of Heaven.
neitz minyan	A quorum reciting the morning prayer at sunrise.
neshamah	Soul.
niggun	Tune, often associated with religious activities.
Nissan	The first month of the Jewish calendar, the month Passover falls in.
olim	Immigrants.
parashas ha'shavua	The Torah portion of the week.
Pesach	Passover.
Pesach Seder	The ritual conducted on Passover night.
Petach Tikva	A city in central Israel not far from B'nei Brak.
protekzia	The Israeli word for "pull" or obtaining privileged and special treatment.
rabbanim	Rabbis, religious educators.
Rambam	Maimonides.
rav	Rabbi.
rebbe	The spiritual leader of a Chassidic group.

rebbei'im	Plural for *rebbi.*
rebbetzin	Wife of the rabbi, or an authoritative female involved in Jewish education.
rebbi	A teacher in a yeshiva or cheder of Torah and religious subjects.
refuah sheleimah	A complete healing.
Ribono Shel Olam	Master of the Universe, i.e., G-d.
Rofei Kol Basar	Healer of All Flesh, i.e., G-d.
Rosh Chodesh	The first of the month; the new moon.
Rosh Hashanah	The Jewish New Year.
Rosh Yeshiva	The spiritual head of the yeshiva.
schlepping	(Yiddish) Dragging things or oneself with difficulty.
sedarim	Plural of Seder.
Seder	The Jewish ritual carried out on the first night of Passover in Israel. In the Diaspora, the Seder takes place on the first two nights of Passover. *Also*, a block of learning time in yeshiva; an order of Mishnayos.
Seder Mishnayos	An order of the Mishnah.
sefarim	Books; Jewish religious books.
seiver panim yafos	With a pleasant face; with a smiling countenance.
seudah	Meal; feast of religious nature.
seudah mafsekes	The last meal before the fasts of Yom Kippur and Tishah b'Av.
seudas hoda'ah	A thanksgiving feast.
Shaarei Orah	Gateways of Light.
Shabbat	Saturday, the Israeli way of pronouncing "Shabbos," the Jewish day of rest.
Shabbos	Saturday, the Jewish day of rest.
Shacharis	The morning prayer.

shadchan	Matchmaker.
shaliach	Messenger.
shalom	Peace; hello.
sheitel	Wig. A married Jewess is obligated to cover her hair by wearing a wig, hat, or scarf.
Shemoneh Esrei	The *Amidah* prayer, recited standing and in silence.
shep nachas	Deriving great pleasure from something; being extremely proud of someone.
sheva berachos	Ritual meal and celebration during the seven days following a Jewish marriage.
shidduch	Matchmaking proposal for marriage; loosely used as a match in any endeavor.
shiur; shiurim	Lesson; lessons; Torah discourses.
shluf shtunda	(Yiddish) Siesta hour.
shul	(Yiddish) Synagogue.
siddur	Jewish prayer book.
simchah	Happiness; a joyous occasion; a celebration.
Simchas Beis HaSho'eivah	
	The Water Libation ceremony performed in the Holy Temple on the Sukkos holiday. It included joyous celebration with music, dancing, acrobatics, etc. Today, in commemoration, *yeshivos* and shuls have a night of music and dancing during Chol Hamoed.
Simchas Torah	The last day of the Sukkos holiday, the day we complete the yearly reading of the Torah. It is celebrated with joyous dancing with the Torah.
siyum	Lit., completion. When finishing learning a section of Torah, Mishnah, or Talmud one celebrates the occasion with a ceremony and festive meal.
sukkah	The booth built for the holiday of Sukkos.

Sukkos	The holiday of Booths, following Yom Kippur.
talmid chacham; talmidei chachamim	
	A Torah scholar; Torah scholars.
Tante	(Yiddish) Aunt.
tefillah; tefillos	Prayer; prayers.
tefillas Minchah	The afternoon prayer.
tefillin	Phylacteries.
Tehillim	Psalms.
tikkun	Rectification, fixing, soul correction.
Tishah b'Av	Ninth of Av, the fifth Jewish month, the day the two Holy Temples in Jerusalem were destroyed. It falls in August.
Tishrei	Seventh Jewish month, in which falls Rosh Hashanah, Yom Kippur, and Sukkos.
Torah	Bible; Pentateuch; body of Jewish learning.
tov	Good.
tzaddik	Holy or righteous person.
tzedakah	Charity.
tzniyus	Modesty in dress, speech, mannerisms, and/or approach to life.
V'samachta b'chagecha	
	And you shall rejoice in your festivals.
Yam Suf	Sea of Reeds; Red Sea.
Yamim Nora'im	The High Holy Days (Rosh Hashanah and Yom Kippur); Days of Awe.
yamim tovim	The Jewish holidays.
yarmulke	Skullcap.

yeridah l'tzorech aliyah

        Lit., descent for the purpose of ascent; Chassidic maxim.

Yerushalayim   Jerusalem.

yeshiva; yeshivos   Jewish religious institution/s of learning.

yeshiva bochur   A teenaged or older but unmarried yeshiva student.

yeshiva gedolah   Yeshiva for seventeen-year-old boys and above.

yeshiva ketanah   Yeshiva for fourteen- to sixteen-year-old boys.

yeshivas bein hazemanim

        A yeshiva learning program during the intercession period.

yeshu'as Hashem k'heref ayin

        The salvation of Hashem is like the blink of an eye.

yetzer hara   The evil inclination.

Yiddishkeit   Judaism.

yiddishe   (Yiddish) Jewish.

Yom Kippur   Day of Atonement, a fast day, considered the holiest day of the Jewish year.

yom tov   Lit., a good day; a Jewish holiday.

Yosef   The Biblical Joseph sold as a slave to Egypt.

zechus   Merit.

Zeidy   (Yiddish) Grandfather.

zeman   Time (for prayers); a block of learning time in yeshiva.

zemer; zemiros   Religious song or songs sung on the Sabbath and holidays.

zivug   Soul mate.

zivug hagun   Fitting, appropriate soul mate.

ABOUT THE AUTHOR

*B*racha Pearl Toporowitch, wife, mother, grandmother, and great-grandmother, was born in London, England. She grew up in Brooklyn, NY, and her high school years were spent under the tutelage of Rebbetzin Vichna Kaplan. After marriage, she lived in Lakewood, NJ, during the time Rav Shneur Kotler, *zt"l*, was Rosh Yeshiva, and then made *aliyah* to Israel with her family. She currently lives in Zichron Yaakov in the north of Israel.

Since 1969, Mrs. Toporowitch has been working with women in various capacities; from 1999, as a guided imagery practitioner and hypnotherapist. She is the founder of the Mind-Body Healing Fertility Clinic in Ramat Beit Shemesh. In addition, she gives *shiurei Torah* in Hebrew and English and always weaves in authentic Jewish *hashkafah* to her work as a practitioner.

Mrs. Toporowitch is the author of *At Your Command*, the riveting account of the life of her father.